GROW IN LIGHT

a parable about
the ancient wisdom of
Silence and Simplicity

Tori

Fiore
P.O. Box 50663
Phoenix, AZ. 85076

Just recently, this story came from the third Hopi Mesa:

An elderly woman, who never spoke, suddenly said one day, "We have visitors." There were three men dressed in white buckskin, and they said:

"THE TIME IS SOON. RETURN TO THE TRADITIONAL WAYS. PRAY. THE TIME IS SOON."

The three men then disappeared.

The following is a parable about a Mystical People who lived differently from how we live now. Each of us has been the various characters in this story.

We have all traveled from a time of innocence, in which we connected with everything through our thoughts, and saw clearly how everything is connected by the Maker of All Things which is in all things.

We have each been those who began to think "separately" from the Maker of All Things, deciding that we could judge good from not-good, and thus did not need to put Maker of All Things first in our thoughts anymore.

We have all been fooled by the illusion of "specialness," which would make us think that we are either superior or inferior to other people, or other aspects of Creation. Whereas, the Maker sees everything as equal parts of the Whole.

We have all had lessons in misusing our power or gifts for our own gain, rather than for the Highest Good of All Involved.

There are some who continue to commune with the Ancestors, Ancient Ones, Holy Spirit, masters, guardians, angels (or whatever one chooses to call them), and gain from the Wisdom of all that has gone before.

The message is usually the same: ALL IS WELL. Put Maker of All Things (or the name you use) first in your thoughts. Then, as you reconnect with the Hub of the Wheel, (the place where all souls meet), you will be able to see from the Divine Mind - rather than from the fearful, limited human perception.

The Divine Mind brings peace, reverence, honor, harmony, balance, kindness, trust, sincerity, humility, oneness.

The human mind can create fear, greed, revenge, unforgiveness, pride, competition, attachment, addictions, possessiveness, anxiety, separateness, war, destruction, and so forth.

How did we get so far off the path from our peaceful beginnings? Thi s is a parable which shares the keys of how human consciousness strayed from the natural harmony. It is not easy to undo all that human society has gotten us used to. The patterns of our thoughts have deep grooves.

Silence and Simplicity are the first steps. Within silence, the Ancient Wisdom can return to all who are willing to listen through the heart. Empty the cup of what you think you know, before beginning this story, and be willing to see anew. Read the story as though an Ancient Storyteller is sharing it with you.

Our choice is simple: do we chose peace or fear? Peace comes from returning to how the Maker of All Things sees life. Fear comes from the 'separate seeing' which the human mind created.

Fear brings illusions.
Illusions bring doubt.
Doubt brings confusion, and confusion brings fear.
Thus the cycle of darkness regenerates itself.

Peace brings stillness.
Stillness brings Knowing.
Knowing brings Truth.
Truth brings Freedom.
Freedom brings Joy.
Joy brings Love.
Love brings Peace.
And so it is we GROW IN LIGHT.

Characters

Key-my-u: daughter of SunWalker and Sparkling Water; granddaughter of Many Stars

Sacred One: spiritual leader of group from Mu

Many Stars: SunWalker's mother; Keymyu's grandmother

Sparkling Water: Keymyu's mother; SunWalker's mate

SunWalker: Keymyu's father; Many Star's son

Laughing Wolf and Steady Turtle: guardians of SunWalker's family

Feathered Trumpet: self-proclaimed leader

Raven: woman companion of Feathered Trumpet

Hawk: friend of SunWalker from beach community

Hummingbird: mate of SunWalker from beach community

Moonbeam: Hummingbird's sister; mate of Hawk

CrowWolf: son of Hummingbird and SunWalker

Gentle Breeze: older woman friend of Raven

KEY-MY-U
record keeper of the Sacred Way

Keymyu awoke to the sound of thunder, and of people screaming. However, it was not the thunder that comes with a rain storm, and the people screaming was unusual, since they had become silent now that they were on this Island with the Sacred One. He had told them that through silence, the People could relearn how to communicate through thoughts, rather than through their mouths. "When one communicates through thought, there can be no lies, because all will know what is true by listening through their heart," he had told them.

The earth rattled and rolled underneath Keymyu. Bits of branches and leaves tumbled upon her head. She stumbled out of her dwelling, wondering what had happened to her mother and grandmother. Today was supposed to have been the time of her becoming a woman, when her mother and father would present her in a Ceremony to her People. She had grown twelve full cycles of seasons.

The thought came from within her to go to the Sacred Cave. Since Sacred One was training them to listen to their inner guidance, she followed the message and moved toward the Cave as best she could, with the earth shaking underneath her.

At the opening of the Cave, a pile of rocks had shaken loose, and now blocked the entrance. Keymyu's heart choked as she recognized her mother's arm outstretched from the pile of rock. She recognized the woven bracelet she had given her mother. Confusion filled her thoughts as she also recognized what was in her mother's hand, the Sacred Feathers!

The Sacred One had told the People that only HE was to touch the Sacred Feathers, and that if anyone else touched

1

them , they would not only experience harm to themselves, but also to their family.

Why was her mother at the Sacred Cave? Why was she holding the Sacred Feathers? Where was Sacred One, and why did HE not have the Feathers? Tears flooded her cheeks, as Keymyu knelt before her mother.

A gentle hand touched her shoulder, and the thoughts of her Grandmother said within her, "Take the Feathers, my child. You are to keep them for Our People. We must go now quickly. Sing your mother back to the Living Light as we run to the dugout waiting for us at the shore."

The firm motion of her Grandmother's hands made Keymyu follow, even though she did not want to leave her mother. Her Grandmother paused for a moment, and folded Keymyu's sleeping robe so that an inner pocket was formed. She had Keymyu place the Feathers in the pocket.

In a fog of numbness, Keymyu barely noticed how the earth was sinking to their left and right, leaving only narrow bridges of land which allowed them to get to the shore. Once there, her Grandmother lifted her into the dugout which was being held by Laughing Wolf and Steady Turtle, the two guardians Sacred One had given to their family. Others pushed their way into the dugout as well; and concentric circles of waves, caused by the earth's rocking, sent the dugout farther and farther away from the shore.

Keymyu could feel the Sacred Feathers against her heart, where her Grandmother had created a pocket. She knew that her Grandmother's thoughts were to hide the Feathers so that no one would become fearful that they were in this dugout, and not with the Sacred One.

With her head cradled against her Grandmother's chest, Keymyu did not look when everyone in the dugout cried out, as the Sacred Mountain exploded. Great clouds of gray dust, wind and lightning began to expand outward from the explo-

2

sion. Tree branches, leaves and all manner of debris filled the air, and landed on the water, and on the people in Keymyu's dugout. They bent low, covering their heads, as giant waves swept them up and down in a gray chalky mist.

"Grandmother," Keymyu said in her thoughts, "Why is this happening to Our People and to the place where we live? Where are we going? What has happened to my father?"

"It is like the Sacred One said, Keymyu," her Grandmother answered in her thoughts. "Do you not remember at the Harvest Moon Gathering, when he told us that a time would come - when that which was land would become water, and that which was water would become land. There were many who grumbled and said that the Sacred One must have had too much ceremonial drink, because surely such a thing could not happen."

"Somehow I knew that what he said was true," her Grandmother continued. "I just did not know the timing...nor did the Sacred One. When telling the story, the Sacred One looked directly into my eyes and my heart, knowing that I understood his words. Then he nodded toward you, and said that you were to be a part of what was to happen. 'You will know what to do when it happens,' his thoughts had said; and that was the end of our communication."

"Why did the Sacred One not go and get the Feathers himself?" asked Keymyu in her thoughts.

"I do not know these things," her Grandmother responded. "I just know that we are in the dugout now, and we will have to trust Maker of All Things to lead us to the next place where our home will be."

Keymyu wondered why she felt that her Grandmother was not telling her everything, but then thoughts of fear took over. "Did anyone bring food and water?" she wondered, but decided not to look around the dugout, for fear that she would not find any. Instead, she focused on the Feathers at her chest

3

and went into a deep sleep.

Cloud Dancer of Inner Vision brought her to a large mound of dirt and rock with very steep steps and large serpents crawling all about. She felt herself being led up the steps in a stupor; and someone with a great feathered headdress was beckoning her to come near. She felt fear, and yet peace at the same time.

People around her had thoughts of how she was being honored in this Ceremony; but their thoughts also held fear about some sort of sacrifice. "Thank you for saving us," she heard from their mouths, but did not understand. She remembered how Sacred One had warned her to beware of those who spoke one thing with their lips, but their heart said the opposite. That must be why she felt apprehension, she thought, because their mouths spoke of praise, while their hearts spoke of danger.

Keymyu felt that she must have been given a strong potion, because her thoughts were foggy, and Cloud Dancer was whirling around her with feathers. "The Sacred Feathers!" she gasped in horror. "How does this Feathered One have the Sacred Feathers? Why am I here on this tall mound of dirt and rock?" She awakened in her Grandmother's arms, shaking with a high fever.

"Be still, my child," she heard from her Grandmother's thoughts. "You have slept for three days in a fever. Are you able to eat?"

"Grandmother, Grandmother," Keymyu could barely form her thoughts. "We must not go to that place. People there cannot be trusted. Their hearts do not say the same meaning as the words from their mouths. Do not take me there, Grandmother...please." But she fell back into Cloud Dancer's arms, and went back into a deep sleep. Her Grandmother knew that this was a fever of inner work, rather than of being sick. The fever heightened her brain waves so that she could sense the inner realms more clearly. Many Stars gently fed her

4

granddaughter the healing liquids which Wolf had placed in the dugout with a few other supplies.

Many moons passed as the People attempted to survive in their dugouts. The winds and waves had separated them. The ones trained in the Sacred Ways asked for guidance from the Maker of All Things, and for help from the elements. They attuned to become one with the Great Spirit, which connects all things. "If it be the will of the Maker of All Things, please bring us food and water," they would pray.

When the rains came, they used the large leaves and other items which had blown into their dugout to gather the fresh water and quench their thirst. When schools of fish swam around their dugout, they thanked the ones that turned on their sides and presented themselves as food.

As Grandmother Many Stars gently fed her grand-daughter, she prayed the many thanks for them both. "The Sacred One taught us well," she thought, "in how to become one with all of life, and to trust that all would be given as we needed it. Sacred One taught us how to call the birds and fish, and four-legged ones when food from Mother Earth became scarce. Knowing that we are all here so that life can continue to be, the various creatures which Maker of All Things made, willingly present themselves so that the Life Force can continue to be in whatever becomes nourished by them."

Many Stars also trusted that Maker of All Things was caring for her granddaughter, as Keymyu went in and out of deep periods of sleep. The times when Keymyu was awake were spent in nourishing her body with food and water, or stretching her limbs in movement. "I need to go back to the Ancient Ones for more teaching," she would mumble, and then drift off again into a deep meditative state.

It seemed like a full cycle of seasons had passed before the dugout with Keymyu, her Grandmother, Wolf and Turtle reached land. It had washed up near the shore when the night

5

was extra dark during the new moon. At daylight, all cheered with joy as they jumped out and pulled the dugout to the sandy shore. Grandmother Many Stars helped her granddaughter walk to the dry beach.

"A new moon, a time for new beginnings," came the thoughts of her Grandmother as Keymyu gently breathed inward. The time of deep inner work was done, and Keymyu knew that her strength would soon return.

"With the Great Spirit's help," Keymyu thought, "my father will also be guided to this distant land." Her prayers went out to not only her father, but also her mother, Sparkling Water, in the Land of Light. She felt her mother's presence all during the journey across the Great Waters. Keymyu spoke with her in her thoughts as though she were still alive.

SPARKLING WATER
one whose innocent love heals naturally

Sparkling Water watched from above, as Keymyu and Many Stars struggled toward the dugout held by the two guardians of their family, Wolf and Turtle. She saw the Sacred Mountain explode, and how her daughter went into a deep sleeping state during the journey across the Great Waters.

"Take my hand," she said to her daughter, as Cloud Dancer lifted Keymyu to the place of Inner Learning. "I have gone before you so that I could lead you to the place where the Ancient Ones share their Wisdom. They will show you how the Original People lived and communicated with all around them through their thoughts, in silence, just as Sacred One was teaching us."

Keymyu followed effortlessly in this dream-state, for she had learned to trust her mother without question, because her mother was one guided by an innocence that wanted nothing for herself, but gained joy by sharing and serving others.

Her father had often remarked how people were naturally drawn to Sparkling Water (the one whose heart sparkled the way water does in the sunlight). He told of how Sparkling Water's gentle words and hands would soothe people's aching bones and muscles. She would go out into the woods and know exactly what flower, berry, leaf or bark to gather and use as a remedy.

Her family felt honored when Sacred One chose her as one of the few he would instruct in the Sacred Healing Ways of the Ancients. "She will listen, whereas others question and doubt because of their strong wills, fear or greed," Sacred One would say. "Her humility allows her to be an open channel so

7

Maker of All Things can create goodness through her. Sparkling Water is not attached to what flows through her, nor does she seek attention for it. She just allows it to flow through her, and then remains open for what will happen next."

Keymyu also remembered how her father spoke warmly of the day when Sacred One told him that he and Sparkling Water would wed. He noticed the shy, yet happy way she smiled at him. Knowing that she had not yet learned the ways of being a woman, SunWalker wisely waited for Sparkling Water to show him when she was ready for mating.

Her father also told her that as a baby, she developed faster in her mother's womb than most babies. He was thrilled when his daughter was born. "I now have two Sparkling Lights in my life," he would say.

"Come now," her mother urged, as Keymyu's thoughts drifted into the past. "The Ancients are ready to teach you the Keys of how and why the People strayed from the Original Ways...a time when Maker of All Things was put first in one's thoughts. Since the Maker is _in_ every aspect of life, one communicated with the Maker, present in every aspect of life. And when one looks through the Maker's Way of Seeing, one understands how everything is connected, and affects every-thing else. But when one looks through the limited human mind, then one interprets everything as separate. This 'separate way of seeing' was what led humans down a self-destructive path. The Ancients will tell you the rest...."

Sensing that her daughter was sad about not knowing where her father was during the explosion of the mountain, Sparkling Water gently whispered in her daughter's thoughts, "SunWalker is alive, and will be protected on his journey, little one. Come now to the place where all souls meet."

8

SUN-WALKER
one who walks with the Inner Light

SunWalker enjoyed practicing the kicks which Sacred One had taught him for self-defense and to focus his mind. His opponent in the game today had a fake knife, but was playing with the intention of outwitting the skillful SunWalker.

A runner entered the playing field just as SunWalker kicked the knife out of the opponent's hand. Before the two could begin again, the runner gave SunWalker an urgent message. "Sacred One wants you to come to his cave immediately," said the runner, and SunWalker thanked him.

Since it was very rare for Sacred One to invite anyone to his cave, SunWalker knew that this must be important. So after bowing to his opponent, honoring the good they had learned together, SunWalker ran to the cave where Sacred One lived.

"The Mountain speaks," said Sacred One as SunWalker approached. "It asks to be heard, and I usually climb the summit to the place where it is warm, even in cold seasons, but my legs are too old to climb those steep cliffs and receive the message. Go for me, SunWalker. You have proven yourself to be one of high honor, one who is clearly guided by the Inner Sun, or Inner Light of Wisdom. Something is about to happen, and the People need to know what to do." Sacred One did not dare tell SunWalker that his own mind was so clouded from worry about what he needed to tell the People tomorrow at the Ceremony, that he could not remain centered enough to understand the urgent message he felt was coming from the Sacred Mountain. The People expected their Sacred One to be above human emotion, always centered; but Sacred One knew there were times when he was not in that space, just like everyone else. To show himself as less than perfect, might create doubt in the People's perception of him as their spiritual leader, he reasoned. He knew that SunWalker was very centered right now, and could therefore bring the message back to the People.

SunWalker wondered why the Sacred One was sending him, since tomorrow was the day when his daughter, Keymyu, would be presented as a woman to her People. He had wanted to be fully rested for that day of Ceremony, but the urgency in Sacred One's manner made him put aside his own wants, and do what was asked of him. Sacred One was just beginning to teach him how to listen to the Spirit of the Land, so SunWalker hoped he could fulfill the request. He knew that Sacred One would not ask him to do anything unless it was for the good of the People; so he immediately started on the journey to the summit.

Fortunately, Laughing Wolf was outside the cave; so SunWalker asked Wolf to tell his mother and wife what Sacred One wanted him to do. "With Great Spirit's help, I will be back in time for my daughter's Ceremony, or we can delay it, if we have to," he added.

As SunWalker walked off to the other side of the mountain where the earth is warm, even in cold seasons, Laughing Wolf remembered a story his father had told him about a time when his father was just a boy. "The Sacred Mountain asked to be heard," his father had said as he de-scribed the Mountain spitting forth a red-hot fiery substance. Wolf wondered if the Mountain was about to "speak" like it did before; so he gathered Steady Turtle, his trusted friend, and prepared a dugout. In case SunWalker's family needed a quick retreat, he would be ready. He also told SunWalker's mother where her son had gone, and how he had a dugout ready in case of any emergency.

Sacred One had chosen Laughing Wolf as a guardian of that family, for just this reason. Wolf had an uncanny way of preparing for things before they actually happened. It was this

10

gift, and his skills as a hunter and tracker, that made him an excellent guard and loyal friend.

SunWalker climbed the cliffs which were embraced by mounds of sand. After finding a level place to sit, he began his prayers; but he had barely uttered a sentence when the earth rumbled gently underneath him for a few seconds. *"Go to the water,"* he heard within, but thought that this might be coming from fear, rather than from the Great Spirit. The earth had been giving these small tremors for three moons now.

He moved away from where he was sitting because it had become hot. As he was about to sit, the earth rumbled again for a few seconds. *"Go to the water,"* he heard again, and the ground under his feet became even hotter.

Retreating a few more yards down the mountain, the earth shook hard enough this time to send him tumbling down on to the soft sand below. As he rolled downward, again he heard, *"Go to the water."*

SunWalker was torn between thoughts of going to see if his wife, daughter, and mother were safe on the other side of the mountain, or doing immediately what was told to him three times: "Go to the water." He decided not to doubt what he had heard, or perhaps something even worse might happen to his People.

So he ran as fast as he could to a place near the water where dugouts were stored by his People, and paddled out away from the island. Just as he turned the dugout around to look back at the island, the Sacred Mountain exploded with clouds of gray dust which eventually encompassed him. Concentric circles of high waves moved him farther and farther away from the island.

Although his thoughts were of rowing back to see if he could find his family, his eyes stung with gray soot, and he was blinded in his efforts.

A piece of flying debris from the great winds of the

11

explosion knocked him unconscious in his dugout. Whirls of white mist filled his mind as Cloud Dancer gathered him up and took him to the place where all souls meet. There he saw the face of Sacred One emerging from a cloud.

"I have passed from the Earth and am in the Land of Light now, as is your wife Sparkling Water and many other people from the Land of Mu, who were killed by the earthquake and explosion. We will guide you on your journey to the new land, where the Sacred Ways must be remembered and followed. Remember what I taught you about becoming at one with all of life around you. By aligning with the Maker of All Things, as you need water, it will be supplied, and as you need food, it will come to you."

SunWalker was awakened as a light rain washed across his face. He drank the fresh water which had collected in the leaves in his dugout, and used the leaves and twigs to make containers to hold as much water as he could collect.

Some of the twigs which had been blown into his dugout by the Great Wind of the explosion had berries on them. He made sure to thank Maker of All Things for all that was supplied to him. There was enough twine to make nets; and when he was hungry, he called the beings of the Great Water to help him, and they presented themselves to be eaten.

All of these things were a natural way of life for the ones who had gone to the island with the Sacred One, for he had taught them the power that comes from the Inner Work. "Focus first on the Inner, and the Outer will come forth from the intention of your heart," were the words of Sacred One. "If you have malice or manipulation in your heart, things will repel away from you. But if you have Love without any wants or fears, all things will feel at peace with you and be drawn to you naturally. There are those who fool people with their outward display of magic. But a wise person will look beyond the outer shell to the inner intention of the heart."

That is why SunWalker was drawn to Sparkling Water, he remembered. Her heart was clear, innocent, with no schemes of wanting, nor any barriers from fearing. He had taken time to get to know her as a good and trusted friend. Soon they realized that they knew each other's thoughts simultaneously. They had become a good team, balancing each other when things around them became stressful. One of the happiest days of SunWalker's life was when his wife gave birth to Keymyu. It was the Sacred One who named her. He told them that they would have a greater understanding of that name in days to come. Since the baby giggled with glee whenever anyone said the name Keymyu, they decided to accept Sacred One's suggestion and gave her that name at the Naming Ceremony.

Without much food or water as the moons passed, SunWalker drifted in and out of sleep, visions, prayers, and memories. Although his human mind wanted to doubt his ability to survive, he kept forcing his thoughts back to trusting the Maker of All Things. He felt Sparkling Water sending him strength and encouragement. She would not let him give in to fear. It felt as though she was right there with him as his companion on this journey.

After what seemed like a full cycle of seasons, Sun-Walker saw what appeared to be land in the distance, and paddled with all his might until he at last reached the shore.

Totally exhausted, he plopped down on to the warm sand, and fell asleep, until awakened by the morning sun. A strange sound caught his attention; and a multi-colored bird flew to a tree nearby to observe this stranger in its territory. He laughed when the bird gave its trumpeting call. Remembering that Sacred One had said to observe the birds and animals for messages, he began to follow the bird into the jungle, but came to a place where large snakes wound themselves around trees and slithered along the ground.

"Great Spirit help my daughter and mother, if they have also landed on this strange land," thought SunWalker. He decided to return to the beach, where he could see the sky more easily, and trusted the waters to provide food as needed.

Footprints eventually led him to others from his homeland who had also been washed up on to this jungled beach. Most of them did not understand his thoughts, so he communicated with the traditional language from the mainland, and gradually realized that they had much in common. They decided to join forces to survive.

Not a day went by that SunWalker did not think of his daughter and mother. Whenever a runner went into the jungle to meet with other bands of people that were gathering in a cleared area, SunWalker would ask the runner if anyone knew of Keymyu or Many Stars, his mother. No one seemed to know anything about them, but SunWalker kept hope in his heart. He just knew that they were alive somewhere, because he could feel their prayers for him, and he sent prayers in return.

FEATHERED TRUMPET
one who proclaims himself as gifted leader

Keymyu, her Grandmother, Laughing Wolf, and Steady Turtle were also greeted by the bird of many colors with a trumpeting call. They followed it into the jungles, as Wolf and Turtle cut away the heavy underbrush. There they found pools of clear water and plants with colorful flowers, berries, and other edible things.

It was not long before they met others who had wandered into the jungle. Many spoke the traditional tongue of Mu from the mainland. Only a very few knew how to communicate through thoughts. When Keymyu and her Grandmother kept quiet most of the time, the other people thought of them as backward, and thus did not mind when the old woman and child chose to live outside the community in a private dwelling. Laughing Wolf and Steady Turtle did most of the hunting, trading and communicating for them; therefore, no one really knew the names of this strange old woman and young girl who never spoke.

Many Stars thought it wise to keep her granddaughter separate from those who were beginning to follow the one who called himself Feathered Trumpet. That was the name many had first given to the multi-colored bird that led them to the crystal pools. Since the People held this bird in reverence for leading them to food and water, the one who had ordained himself as leader, decided to take the name of Feathered Trumpet for himself.

If the truth were told, most of the people let Feathered Trumpet take over because they were afraid of him. He had a temper which thundered loudly and suddenly like a rain storm, and he was a better hunter and more skilled with a knife than

15

any of them. So to challenge Feathered Trumpet, would have meant a certain death to the challenger.

Keymyu felt that Feathered Trumpet's ways were against the Ancient teachings she had learned during the dream-state on the journey across the Great Water. "Better to be invisible like the wind, than crushed like an ant," her Grandmother said. So she only told her Grandmother about the Ancient teachings, and let the other People learn what they needed to learn by following the self-appointed one.

According to the Ancient Ways, a natural leader was never self-appointed. To do so meant false pride - a quality which a natural leader should not have. It was the People who chose the Leader, by observing who would do the Highest Good for all involved. A natural leader would express ideas to guide the people, rather than force them into anything. A natural leader used his skills in hunting, reasoning, and creating things so that all gained from them. He would not accumulate wealth, status or possessions unto himself, but would make sure that a natural balance and harmony came about in dividing the food, clothing, tools, chores, etc. When a certain project needed to be done which would be good for the whole community, the People gladly participated, because a good leader praised, encouraged and honored all for their unique way of contributing.

Feathered Trumpet seemed to lead with the opposite approach. He ordered things to be done, with threats of punishment, if they were not done. Thus, when he commanded that a large pile of rock and dirt be built, which would eventually tower above the forest, the People begrudgingly did the task. "It will allow us to be closer to the sky and Maker of All Things," Feathered Trumpet would say; but the People really knew that he was building it to keep a look-out for any enemy who might want to take away his possessions or leadership.

Each day Feathered Trumpet would take food or precious items and place them at the top of the Great Mound as an offering to the Creator. By doing so, he told the People, this would keep them safe and protected. However, when the rainy season came, an unknown sickness began killing the People.

"If you have the powers you say you have," some argued to Feathered Trumpet, "then you should be able to stop this sickness. But more and more of our People die every day!" Feathered Trumpet was at a loss in knowing what to do. All he could think of was, "We need a greater sacrifice to Maker of All Things. I will go and pray and fast, and come back with an answer," he told the People.

After three days and three nights of prayers and fasting, Feathered Trumpet still had no answer. However, while wandering back to the village, he caught sight of someone walking in a direction where he knew of no path. "I wonder where that person is going," he thought.

Keymyu was on her daily journey to where she had hidden the Sacred Feathers. She would pray with them, and surround them with the smoke of burning sweet grass, as she asked for protection for her family, and for Wolf and Turtle.

Feathered Trumpet could not see clearly what she was taking from behind a rock because her body blocked his view. After this young girl left the area, he went to the rock where she had been, and moved it to one side. His heart laughed with delight when he recognized the Sacred Feathers that Sacred One had taken with him to an unknown island with a group of people. Ever since that day, the mainland of Mu had suffered terrible chaos. The People had fights, accidents, and many died or lost their faith. But now that he, Feathered Trumpet, had this Sacred treasure, all good things would return to the People, and the unknown sickness would end in this new land, he assured himself.

He would have to find out who that young girl was, and perhaps use her when they gave a sacrifice to the Powers that be. Yes, that was it, one of their own People would be the greatest sacrifice that they had ever made. This, plus the

17

Sacred Feathers, will surely turn things in his favor. Besides, since the young girl is probably the only one who knows about the Feathers, then she must be eliminated so that all believe that the Feathers came to him during his three days of fasting and praying.

Only for a moment did he wonder how this young girl got the Sacred Feathers, and then dismissed the thought, reasoning that she probably had no idea what she had. How would a young girl know of such things; and if the Sacred One were still alive, HE would have the Feathers himself.

"Wait until I show these to Raven," he thought. "She has always been interested in things of Power. That is why she chose me, the one who took power over the People. She will have to show me much pleasure to touch these." With these final thoughts, Feathered Trumpet returned home, feeling proud and triumphant.

RAVEN
one who uses power for their own gain

When Feathered Trumpet placed the Sacred Feathers on the bed before her, Raven did not know whether to laugh or cry. She looked down at the scar on her hand, which she received the last time she laid eyes on these very Feathers. Her thoughts went back to a time when the Sacred One had danced with both her and Sparkling Water at the Summer Feast. It had been rumored that the Sacred One would choose to teach two people who had shown the natural ability for healing.

Raven knew that both she and Sparkling Water had helped people who came to them with ailments. This was well known in the village.

At the end of the Feast, the Sacred One asked both Raven and Sparkling Water to come to his cave for teaching. Raven agreed to go, but went not for teachings. She went to beguile the Sacred One into moments of pleasure. She was well skilled in capturing men's hearts, who would then possessively do anything in order to keep her.

All day she tried to take the Sacred One's mind off the teachings. She could learn all of that later, she thought. But all her efforts failed, and she left in a huff at sundown.

The next day, Raven followed Sparkling Water to the Cave. "This one knows nothing of pleasure," Raven thought. "She is a woman with a girl's innocence. Everyone knows that she has been seeing SunWalker for over six moons and they do not even touch each other. Surely, this one will not gain Sacred One's favor."

The following day, Sacred One visited the place where women washed clothing. He place the Sacred Feathers between

19

Raven and Sparkling Water. "Let us see who the Feathers choose," he said.

Sparkling Water moved back away from the Sacred Feathers. She did not understand. Had not the Sacred One said that these Feathers should never be on the ground, and that if anyone touched them, other than him or a rightful heir, that they would bring harm to that person and their family?

Raven laughed at what she interpreted as Sparkling Water's cowardice. "I am not afraid of these Feathers," she said. "I am a healer with great power myself, and therefore would be a natural heir to hold and use them." But as she reached her hand down to pick the Feathers up, a circle of fire surrounded them and burnt Raven's hand. She quickly withdrew her hand and covered it with the garment she had been washing.

"The Feathers have chosen," said Sacred One as he picked them up and took Sparkling Water by the hand, leading her away.

All Raven knew after that was that Sparkling Water had spent the evening with Sacred One, and within a few days, Sparkling Water and SunWalker were wed - to everyone's surprise.

Shortly thereafter, the Sacred One and a group of people disappeared from the mainland of Mu. There were so many islands around the mainland, that it would have taken ten times ten full cycles of the moon to find them.

Raven also knew Feathered Trumpet during that time; but he was called Led By the Storms in those days. Who would have imagined that this young man with a stormy disposition would one day command the People. That was exactly what he did, she thought. He commanded the People to do things; he did not lead them, nor did they follow of their own free will. How different he was from the Sacred One.

"But none of this matters now," she reasoned. "I will eventually win the People's trust over by my abilities to heal and see people's fear. As well, they are becoming dependent on the potion I have created, which is drunk with every meal. It is this very potion which has dulled their minds so that Feathered Trumpet can rule over them."

She glanced down again at the scar on her hand and the Sacred Feathers. She was not sure she wanted to touch those Feathers right now. She needed time to prepare. So she simply replied to Feathered Trumpet by saying, "I am hungry. Let's go and eat," and she walked out of the dwelling.

This action confused Feathered Trumpet, but then he reasoned: "How clever this woman is to pretend that she is not interested in these powerful Feathers."

He called a guard and told him to go and get the young girl who lived in the only dwelling outside the village. She was going to be honored as part of a Great Ceremony which would bring health back to the People. But the guard knew the real intention of gathering the girl, for he had overheard Raven and Feathered Trumpet talking about a human sacrifice being needed to appease the Powers that be. He had never heard of a human sacrifice before, but who was he to understand the power of magic. So he did as he was told and went to get the young girl who never spoke.

MANY STARS
one who communes with the Ancestors

Many Stars squawked out words of protest from a mouth and throat which rarely spoke. She and her granddaughter understood each other perfectly without the need for words, and thus they rarely talked out loud.

Immediately upon the arrival of this guard, Many Stars discerned from his heart that the so-called Sacred Ceremony which was supposed to honor her granddaughter would actually bring danger to Keymyu.

Both Laughing Wolf and Steady Turtle were away on a hunting trip that day. No one had bothered their private dwelling before, so why would this guard want to take Keymyu away now?

Keymyu vaguely saw the picture of something long and tall in the guard's mind, as she struggled to release herself and run to the safety of her Grandmother's arms. But the guard held fast and jerked her out the doorway and down the path, back to the village.

Keymyu suddenly understood what she was seeing in the guard's mind. "The Feathers!" She projected these thoughts back to her Grandmother. "Go see if the Feathers are still in their hiding place!"

Her Grandmother choked in horror, and quickly ran down the path to where the Sacred Feathers were hidden. Seeing that they were gone, she decided to follow the guard and her granddaughter. All the way there, she put out a distress call mentally to Wolf and Turtle. "Great Spirit, please alert anyone who can help," she added.

Many Stars followed the guard to a tent-like dwelling. As she peeked through a slit on the jungle side of the tent, she saw a beautiful woman with long black hair, stirring some kind of liquid, and then force her granddaughter to drink it. It was all that Many Stars could do to keep from screaming out; but the strong guard was also there, and she had no one to help rescue her granddaughter.

Many Stars made sure that no one saw her, as various people walked in and out of the tent, bathing, dressing and preparing Keymyu for some sort of Ceremony. Tears filled her eyes as she watched her granddaughter's head droop. Obviously she had been given something so that she would not protest or run away.

When the final time had come to take Keymyu to the tall mound of rock and dirt, Many Stars searched the crowd of faces to see if there was anyone whom she knew who could help her. But the People's eyes were glazed over, and even when Many Stars recognized people, they did not recognize her in return, but kept mumbling something about a sacrifice to restore the health of the People.

As Keymyu was led up the steep steps, she almost fell backwards. Many Stars pressed forward to go to her granddaughter's rescue, but was held back by a guard at the base of the Great Mound.

"This cannot be happening," she cried within herself. "This horrible day could not be the destiny of Our People. Great Ancestors, please help me!"

SunWalker moved with the wave of people that were gathering around the Great Mound. He had traveled here with three companions who were like brothers to him. They joined him to find out what this new Ceremony was all about. Sun-Walker had been feeling anxious for the past three days. It has something to do with the Ceremony, he kept thinking. Why do the People think they need something new rather than following the proven ways of the Sacred One?

Upon his arrival at the village, the People graciously provided him and his companions with food and drink. The food tasted good, prepared in the old way, but he hesitated about their drink, since he noticed a strange behavior in those who consumed it. The ones who drank the fragrant liquid did not seem to know their own thoughts. He chose instead to drink the water he had brought, and motioned for his friends to do the same.

Now that the crowd of people had pulled him to the base of the Great Mound, he could see the back of a young girl with flowers in her hair, being led up the steep steps. When she nearly tripped twice, his natural instinct was to go to her aid. Although the crowd was tightly woven together, SunWalker decided to work his way closer.

"Mother," he thought, as memories came forth of the many times she had told him stories about the Ancestors before he went to sleep. "What would the Ancestors say about such a Ceremony?"

"They would send lightning sounds from the stars," his mother's thoughts came into his mind.

Startled by the response, SunWalker searched the sea of faces. Could it be that his mother is alive and here?

"SunWalker!" his mother exclaimed when she finally realized that she was not making up this conversation in her mind.

The crowd crying "Ohhhhh," brought both of their attention back to the young one being led up the steps. She had fallen backward, caught again by the guards, but her face dangled backward, and all could see who she was.

"Keymyu!" shrieked SunWalker, and simultaneously, his mother let out a high pitched shrill that the Ancestors of Sacred One used to make - to silence, balance, and heal the People. An ancient memory ignited within the People in the crowd, because they all turned toward the one making the sound, bowed their heads and remained still as the tones moved

24

through them like a tuning fork. They remembered that when Sacred One sounded these tones, all good things would come to the People, if they bowed their heads and attuned in reverence. Therefore while focusing on the tones, they were unaware of SunWalker racing up the mound to rescue his daughter.

However, Feathered Trumpet was fully aware of what was happening. Followed by Raven, he raced down the steps to reach the young girl before the stranger did. Raven did not care about the girl nor the stranger; she decided to use the confusion of the moment to take possession of the Feathers. She had carefully prepared herself with potions and spells of protection, so that touching the Feathers would not harm her this time.

SunWalker arrived at his daughter only seconds before Feathered Trumpet. The guards who had their heads bowed and were toning with the sacred sounds, suddenly snapped out of that state, and struggled with the stranger who was trying to take the young girl.

After lying Keymyu down, SunWalker used the feet kicks which Sacred One had taught him, to knock the guards unconscious. "The Feathers," he faintly heard in his head in the voice of his daughter; and as Feathered Trumpet lunged toward him with a knife, SunWalker instantly recognized the Sacred Feathers in his other hand. He knew that his daughter was telling him to rescue the Feathers as well.

With a skillful kick, he sent the Feathers arching into the air, out of Feathered Trumpet's hand. As Raven reached for them, she suddenly recognized SunWalker; and her moment's hesitation allowed him to kick the Feathers upward again, while he knocked Raven and Feathered Trumpet into each other and into unconsciousness. Then catching the Feathers and placing them in his daughter's hands, he swiftly moved down the Great Mound.

Many Stars thanked the Ancestors as she continued the toning which kept the people bowed in reverence. She could sense that someone had moved in behind her, but stayed focused in toning the sounds.

SunWalker's friends joined him as he raced into the jungle. The Feathers in his daughter's hands seemed to point the direction they should take. Knowing the power of them, he followed whichever way they pointed, and his companions disguised the path they took.

However, one who is the most skilled in trail finding, managed to read the signs clearly. Laughing Wolf had returned to the dwelling when feeling Many Star's distress call. Her footprints led him to the Great Mound where a crowd had gathered, and a young one was being led up the steps. By her gait, Wolf immediately knew that it was Keymyu, and that her Grandmother must be nearby.

When the Ancient Sounds came forth, and the crowd faced toward Many Stars, it was easy for Wolf to get close to her. He watched SunWalker rescue his daughter, and knew that he must do the same for Many Stars. So the moment the Sacred Sounds ended, Wolf shouted to the People, "Look, Feathered Trumpet has been hurt, and the one who took the maiden went that way," pointing in the opposite direction SunWalker took. In all the confusion when the People were trying to help Feathered Trumpet, Wolf carefully led Many Stars away to safety.

Wolf listened quietly as Many Stars told him what he must tell SunWalker when he found him. When they arrived at Many Star's dwelling, they found that Steady Turtle had returned at his usual slower pace. After quickly gathering supplies for traveling, they started out after SunWalker. Wolf raced ahead to give SunWalker the urgent message from his mother, while Steady Turtle (equally skilled in trail finding) followed at a pace that was easier for Many Stars.

SunWalker had reached a ravine. He and his friends needed to stop and catch their breath. As the companions stood guard, SunWalker placed his daughter on some soft grass. She struggled to form the thoughts that she needed to tell him.

"My father, my heart soars to see you again, but we have little time left together. They gave me a liquid that would not only numb me from being able to run away, but would also eventually kill me. Take these Feathers, my father, and use them for the inward journey to the Ancient Ones. Then you must lead our People back to the Sacred Ways...." Her thoughts drifted off into Cloud Dancer's mist, so no more words came.

SunWalker was startled. Was he going to lose his only daughter after just finding her? Are the Feathers bringing her death, since they were told that no one should hold them except Sacred One or their rightful heir?

His thoughts were interrupted by the sound of a scuffle behind him. "He says you know him." said one of Sun-Walker's friends, who was holding Wolf's arms behind him in a deadly grip.

It took only seconds for SunWalker to recognize the face of the guardian the Sacred One had provided for his family. "Yes," SunWalker acknowledged. "Let him go. He is a friend." And immediately he embraced Laughing Wolf.

"I bring you an urgent message from your mother," began Wolf. Then looking around, added, "Only you should hear these words." So SunWalker walked a ways off with Wolf, motioning for the others to keep an eye on his daughter.

"Your mother said that I must tell you these things as close to her words as I can. So I will do my best. She began this way:"

"My son, it is with great peace and also sorrow that I tell you these things. On the night the Sacred Mountain exploded in our homeland, I was awakened by Sparkling Water leaving our dwelling. You had gone on the journey that Sacred One had requested, so why would Sparkling Water leave in the middle of the night with an arrow in her hand? She is not one to even touch such a thing."

"I felt compelled to follow her, after making sure that Keymyu was sound asleep. I followed her into the Sacred Cave. There she was confronting Sacred One. She wanted to know what had happened the night that she had spent with him, just before he insisted that she marry you, SunWalker. Shortly after that, we all went to the Island of the Heated Mountain. Ever since that evening, Sparkling Water wondered if Keymyu was really your child, but was afraid to tell anyone."

SunWalker's face showed horror at what he was hearing. "Wait!" Wolf urged. "Many Stars said that you would react this way, but wanted you to listen to the rest, before you came to any conclusions." SunWalker decided to let Wolf continue.

"While Sparkling Water was talking, it brought back a memory when I, Many Stars, had been invited to the cave where the Sacred One lived. I was just a young girl. After eating a magnificent meal with Sacred One, I felt drowsy and must have fallen asleep, because the next thing I knew, it was morning, and I was alone in the cave. I went to the river to bathe, and then went home. Soon after this, Sacred One urged me to wed your father, which was fine with me because we deeply loved each other. But it startled my family since I was so young."

"Sparkling Water's conversation made me begin to remember how I had had a child very soon after being wed to your father. So I decided to wait outside and speak with her privately."

"That was when the earth first began to rumble. Since stones and dirt were dropping on my head, I raced outside, fearful for Sacred One and Sparkling Water who were still inside the cave."

"Again the earth shook and I could hear Sparkling Water's screams as she ran toward the entrance. The moment

28

she saw me, she barely got the word 'Keymyu' out while extending forth her hand with the Sacred Feathers."

"With the third tremor, rocks from the cave's entrance piled upon Sparkling Water and her last thoughts to me were while she was still alive, buried under the rocks. 'Sacred One is dead,' she said. 'He threw these Feathers toward me just as the cave ceiling crashed down upon him. His thoughts said that Keymyu and SunWalker are the rightful heirs. I raced out of the cave as fast as I could. Make sure that Keymyu gets these Feathers,' and she died."

"I felt that my questions had been answered. Both Keymyu and SunWalker were seeded by Sacred One, to pass on the lineage of the Ancient Ones who came from the Sun."

"Enough!" SunWalker commanded, "I do not want to hear anymore," and he stormed away kicking the dirt and gravel underneath his feet. But one kick was too strong, for it sent him falling down into the ravine where his head hit on a rock.

Cloud Dancer swirled around him in vision mists. "Is this the only way we can get your attention?" came the voice of Sacred One. "Do you always need to be hit on the head in order for your heart to listen?"

SunWalker did not want to hear the sound of Sacred One's voice. He tried to whirl it away in the mist with his arms. "How can I ever believe anything you taught me after learning how you tricked my wife and my mother that way. You must be the Trickster, rather than the Sacred One. Why was I not told that Keymyu is my sister, not my daughter!"

His mother's face and voice came forward through the mist. "I have prayed to Maker of All Things for help, Sun-Walker, so if you can hear me now, know that it is from the point where all souls connect, and listen carefully."

"You can heal Keymyu if you allow your heart to return to Love, and there is very little time left. So allow your-

self to feel how the Love of the Maker of All Things knows no favorites. The Maker loves daughters and sisters, fathers and mothers, sons and grandchildren, all the same. Whether Keymyu is your daughter or your sister, do you not still <u>love</u> her?"

"Sacred One thought carefully before choosing who should carry on his work and the Sacred Ways. He chose two women with pure hearts, who would not use the power for their own advantage, but would consider the Highest Good for All Involved."

"After releasing my own anger, I realized that Sparkling Water and I had that quality, and that we would instill the same ideals in our children. You and Keymyu are to walk hand in hand as equals, as Brother and Sister, to help the People remember the Sacred Ways. Since you are older, when you pass from the Earth to the Land of Light, Keymyu can continue with the next generation. Thank the Sacred One for his wise choice. I am honored to be your Mother, SunWalker. If I am unable to catch up with you, then know that my prayers and the help of the Ancestors will be with you. Go and heal Keymyu with the Love of the Maker of All Things, and then quickly continue on your journey."

Laughing Wolf was rubbing SunWalker's head as his eyes opened. "No need to continue, Wolf," SunWalker sighed. "I got the rest of the message directly from my mother. Now I must go and give my energy to Keymyu."

All joined in a circle around him as he held Keymyu. They extended their hands inward to lend their own energy. SunWalker asked Maker of All Things to help him. "Show me what to do," he humbly asked.

"Just BE Love," came the words within his heart. "You need DO nothing. Just BE the presence of Love with no wants and no fears."

SunWalker surrendered to the Inner Message and felt the glow of Love radiate out from him, embracing Keymyu and the circle of friends, then expand to include the jungle they were in, the world, and even the Universe. He could feel Keymyu's heartbeat get stronger. He thanked Maker of All Things and just basked in the glow of Love for what seemed like a long time, until Keymyu's words brought his awareness back to the jungle.

"Thank you, SunWalker," Keymyu whispered. "Your radiant Love has removed the toxins from my body. I feel my natural energy returning. And I have heard all about us, while on the inner realm. Know that I will love and honor you as my bother - the same as I loved and honored you as my Father. Let us go, hand in hand, to the new land. And may we carry on the Wisdom and Ways of the Sacred Feathers." She handed them to SunWalker, and he hugged her and wept.

Keymyu continued whispering in SunWalker's ear, "While you were sending me the energy of Love, Sacred One showed me his life and why he made the decisions he did. It is not for me to tell you that story. I think Sacred One should tell you his reasons himself."

"After we have traveled a safe distance, I hope you can find it in your heart to go within and listen to Sacred One. He will take you through the journey as though you were with him making the decisions of what to do for the People. Once you see the obstacles in his way, maybe you will understand."

"He truly regrets what he did, and he was trying to work out how he would tell the People on the day of my Becoming a Woman ceremony, when messages from the Sacred Mountain tried to come forth. However, since he was not centered, due to worrying about what to tell the People and how they might reject him, he could not become clear enough to understand what the Spirit of the Mountain was trying to tell him."

"Thus he called for you, SunWalker, to receive the urgent message. Sacred One knew that where the mountain gets hot is where one hears the Mountain Spirit the clearest. He also knew that your heart was clear and open, so you could bring the information to the People. That is why he sent you away on the evening the Mountain exploded."

"Sacred One became even more clouded within, and out of balance, when Sparkling Water came to him and demanded to know if I, Keymyu, was really his child. He was just beginning to explain to her why certain things were done by him and his Ancestors, when rocks from the cave above him came tumbling down. He threw the Sacred Feathers to Sparkling Water and told her that you and I are the rightful heirs to continue the Work; but both Sacred One and Sparkling Water were buried under rocks from the earthquake."

"So, you see, if his thoughts had not been clouded with human emotions and the fear of rejection for what he and his Ancestors had done, he would have seen what was going to happen and would have warned the People so that all could have gotten off the Island in time. That is the dilemma between the human and the Divine. When we are free of human emotion, we see clearly; but when our human mind is filled with self-doubt and fear, we do not grasp what we need to know, or see what we need to see."

"What do you mean 'what he and his Ancestors had done'?" asked SunWalker.

"That is something Sacred One needs to tell you," Keymyu continued. "Enough for now. I sense that someone is looking for our trail. It is someone who wants the power of the Sacred Feathers. We must move on quickly. Wolf will hide our trail."

SunWalker also felt the urgency of moving on to a safer place, and thus gathered the group together for instructions. Keymyu wanted to force herself to walk in order to bring oxygen and life back into her brain and muscles. One of SunWalker's companions scouted the area ahead of them, while Wolf took up the rear and skillfully covered their tracks.

As he walked, SunWalker allowed Keymyu's wisdom to penetrate his angry heart. Perhaps he did not know the whole story. Yes, he decided, when they had a day's journey behind them, he would take the time to commune with Sacred One on the inner realm and seek to understand what had happened from a broader perspective.

SACRED ONE
one who works to balance the human and the Divine

The sun was about to set when SunWalker's group came upon a magnificent waterfall. They stood in its mist and splashed each other in the pools below the falls.

In his heart, SunWalker knew that this was the perfect place to seek Sacred One on an inner journey. After bathing with the others, he climbed the rocks near the waterfall and found a quiet alcove facing the East.

After settling himself and relaxing his mind and weary muscles, he breathed in deeply, and with the outward breath, made the sound of wind going through an ancient canyon. He did this three times, each time placing his awareness in the center of the wind.

He then allowed a beam of light from his heart to become a spoke of a giant wheel of light. As he traveled through that beam of light to the Hub of the Wheel, his energy molecules became lighter and lighter until he was in the Center of the Hub, the place where all souls meet and are one.

"Sacred One," he barely whispered in his thoughts, since this is a realm where thoughts are not as focused as in the human realm.

"I am here with you," replied Sacred One. "I know your request, and I will show you my life choices based on what those before me had done. Allow yourself to merge with me and see through my eyes."

SunWalker found himself stepping into Sacred One's light form and then traveling back in time with him.

"As you see," Sacred One continued, "When I was a boy, I was trained by my elders. They showed me how human beings had evolved on this planet. Those in the realm of non-form wanted to increase the awareness of those in form.

34

They started by giving humans ideas of how to better their lives, and rules by which to live in peace and harmony with all around them."

"When inspiration or new ideas came into a human's mind, the human saw it as something separate because it was different from how things were done before. There always seemed to be a tug of war between those who wanted to change things and those who wanted to keep things the way they had been. (The tug of war was often between those who had power and those who wanted to bring equality.)"

"To convince the ones who wanted things to remain the same, the newer thinkers had to create or show increased benefits for changing things. Unfortunately, they found that the best way to do this was to show how a human being's sensations would be satisfied to a greater degree: the sensation of safety, or the enjoyment of food, drink, sex, power, greater knowing, greater skills. The indulgence in physical sensation eventually made many humans addicted to sensation. Once their brain had recorded a new sensation and liked it, they wanted it again and again, and then better and better, or greater and greater."

"Focusing on sensation is what led many humans away from we-ness (or what is best for the whole) and toward me-ness (or what is best for me). So when one did not get what one wanted, one began to blame 'you', or something outside one's self for all that was wrong in their life. Before that time, groups of humans had learned to think in terms of WE rather than ME. They truly enjoyed what was best for the greater whole, rather than just focusing on their own personal satisfaction."

"The most Ancient Ones actually focused on looking through the Creator's way of seeing life. Thus they saw how everything is connected and could communicate with all aspects of life, since they communicated with the Creative Spirit which is in every aspect of life."

35

"To help humans return to the Ancient Sacred Ways, the non-form beings needed to send inspired leaders, now and then, to bring humans back to center, back to thinking of how one's actions affect the whole."

"The inspired (or spiritual) leaders had to make rules, and then had to try to follow those rules the best they could. For example, spiritual teachers were trying to undo the human lust for taking sexual pleasure whenever one wanted (even if it hurt another human being)."

"One spiritual leader shared how a Sacred One could rise above the desire for human sex. And soon humans challenged their spiritual leaders to prove it themselves, and to not have sex themselves."

"Schools were formed to try to train people to return their consciousness to spiritual ways, and the Sacred Ones (or teachers) were expected to be free of human desires. But the dilemma which occurred was that those with a more enlightened awareness could not mate, and thus enlightened children were not being born. Those who had the most off-spring seemed to be those who were the most aggressive and who refused to follow or listen to spiritual ways."

"Thus more and more aggressive humans were being reproduced, and less and less spiritually enlightened beings were coming forth. Whatever the children saw their parents do, they did also; so aggressive parents were creating aggressive children."

"One Sacred Brotherhood decided to try to correct the situation by secretly seeding women who had proven to be spiritually advanced. By doing so, enlightened beings would not completely die out from the population. With less and less spiritual teachers available, there were very few left to pass on the teachings and keep the balance."

"As you see, when I was older, I questioned my elders and asked why they could not just let go of the rule that spiritual teachers had to live without sex. Why did they not

allow the spiritual leaders to be examples of responsible sexual behavior?"

"The elder replied that to change a rule would mean that the rule was wrong in the first place; thus people would begin to question every rule that had been made. Then the people might also begin to question the teachings of the spiritual leaders and their schools, and even get rid of them. The Brotherhood did not want to give up their way of life. The community gave them donations so that they did not have to work, but spent all their time in spiritual prayer, studies, or teaching others."

"So you see, pride and the fear of loss perpetuated the lie. I also had become accustomed to that lifestyle and did not want to have to give it up, nor did I want to destroy it for the Brotherhood. I could see the good we were doing in keeping the balance and creating a sanctuary for advanced beings. But I never liked the lie that I knew about, and would one day have to participate in."

"For a week before Keymyu's Becoming a Woman Ceremony, I struggled within my conscience. When it came time for the Father to step forward in the ceremony, I knew it should have been me, not you, SunWalker. I had come to honor you, and Sparkling Water, and Many Stars, and did not want to perpetuate the lie that had been hidden for centuries by the Sacred Order to which I belonged."

"My mind kept wrestling with the possibility that everyone would abandon all the teachings I had been doing, which I knew would help humanity return to goodness and balance. How would people forgive me for the secret way women had been seeded?"

"That is why I could not become centered enough to understand what the Spirit of the Mountain was trying to tell me. My mind was filled with so much emotion and fear of rejection that I could not see or hear anything else. I could not even see that by staying in the Sacred Cave, I would not only cause my own death, but that of Sparkling Water as well. What would you have done, SunWalker?"

SunWalker could feel all the inner turmoil, all the guilt, and yet wisdom that Sacred One had been sharing with the People. He had watched how many had turned their lives and hearts around to goodness and balance because of Sacred One's teachings. He also saw how Sacred One had disobeyed the Brotherhood's vow of keeping the mysteries to themselves. Sacred One was teaching the People, who had followed him to the Island, all the ancient teachings which only the Sacred Brotherhoods were allowed to know before.

SunWalker could also see how telling the truth about how the women had been seeded for centuries might have destroyed the Sacred Order, the Schools, and even the teachings, since the People would feel betrayed and thus begin to doubt all they had been taught. Perhaps even the aggressive ones would have taken over the world and wiped out the gentle ones.

What a choice! SunWalker realized. What would he need to do now, he finally realized. Now is the only moment there is. What happened is in the past. What decisions would he make for the future?

"I guess I can only tell you what I feel that I need to do now," SunWalker began. "I will continue to listen to the Sacred Feathers and Ancient Ones for the teaching of how we can return to the natural balance and harmony with all of life. I will no longer use the term Sacred One, nor have a Brotherhood where only a few learn the Sacred Ways. Instead, I will be an example of responsible action. I will show people how their every thought, word, and action creates a reaction; and thus they need to be responsible for how they affect others and the world around them."

"I will tell them," continued SunWalker, "that immature beings think only of ME; whereas, mature beings think and see in terms of WE. Only immature beings blame some thing or someone outside themselves; whereas, mature beings look to see how they themselves might be responsible for what is happening to them."

"Well done, SunWalker," responded Sacred One. "You are indeed a good leader, and Keymyu will assist you in all that you have to give. If you have learned all this from my life, then I have done the job I came here to do."

"You have also uncovered the meaning of Keymyu's name: the KEY to how humanity strayed away from the Creator was when humanity developed the concept of MY and of YOU. In other words, instead of seeing in terms of how we can serve each other by allowing the goodness of the Creator to work through us, humans invented possessiveness and began referring to things as MY home, MY wife, MY talents, etc.. They also invented the scapegoat of YOU; or it is YOU who made me weak, unhappy, and so forth."

"The name Key-my-u is the key of how to bring the People back to harmony and balance with all of life," concluded Sacred One.

Now SunWalker understood why Sacred One had urged him to call his daughter Key-my-u. SunWalker knew that the peace he now felt toward Sacred One was because he had gained the lessons Sacred One had come to teach him. "I will share the mysteries of the Sacred Schools with all the People," SunWalker said to Sacred One, as he watched his friend (and Father) merge into the golden light. "The People will act more wisely if they learn how to quiet the mind and go within. Thank you for teaching us how to do this...Father."

As Sacred One merged with the light, SunWalker saw a vision of the friends he had made on the beach. "Hummingbird," he sighed as he opened his eyes and felt the mist of the waterfall against his skin. " I have not forgotten you, my soul's delight. I will send Hawk to bring you and our friends on this journey East to our new homeland."

After stretching his legs, SunWalker climbed down the rocks and joined the group for a feast that Laughing Wolf was preparing from his hunt. After the meal, SunWalker asked Hawk to return to their community of friends on the beach, and lead them here, to join this group. Hawk was glad to return and get his wife, Moonbeam, and their other friends. He packed some supplies, and began his journey. He was careful to take a different route in hopes of confusing anyone tracking them.

HUMMINGBIRD
one who humbly serves the Greater Good

As the ocean waves created a mist against Hummingbird's face, she sensed SunWalker's presence, and knew that he would be sending for their group of friends. "It feels like we are going to be taking a long journey," she told Moonbeam, her sister. Then suddenly, a wave of nausea filled Hummingbird's throat, and before she could stop herself, she vomited over the cliff.

"That is three mornings in a row that you have been sick," observed Moonbeam. "I sense my sister is with child."

"I hope he likes adventure," Hummingbird smiled, "because it may be many moons before we settle down from our journey."

"You already know it's a boy?" Moonbeam questioned.

"A Crow and a Wolf in my dreams told me so," answered Hummingbird. "He is to protect something very Sacred from misuse of power. That is all I know for now. Time will tell. Let's go gather things for our journey so that when Hawk arrives, we can leave right away."

"How do you know that it is Hawk who is coming?" Moonbeam asked. She had sensed that herself, but wondered if it was wishful thinking, since she greatly missed her mate and wanted him home soon.

"The same way you knew," Hummingbird giggled as she tickled her sister, and then ran back to their community of friends. She would be glad when she could tell SunWalker that their son was on his way. Moonbeam followed down the cliff at a slower pace. She was sending prayers for a safe journey to her husband. A hawk's screech in the distance made her smile. "Good day to you too," she sighed. "Take care of my husband."

41

As Hummingbird began gathering tools and supplies, memories of her childhood came forth. She and her family had been part of the group which followed Sacred One to the Island. He had told the few which he gathered, that some of the patterns of the old way needed to change in order for the People to heal themselves from all the chaos that was beginning to happen.

""I will teach you the Ancient Ways that only the Sacred Brotherhood knew before. It is time for all the people to know how to go within and listen to the Maker of All Things. By learning how to do this, you will know how to discern false teachings for the Truth. Misguided ones will not be able to manipulate you through fear. You will learn how to trust in the Creator above all else."

Hummingbird remembered how some people on the main island were beginning to hoard wealth and possessions unto themselves, rather than sharing with the community. They then bought and trained guards to protect themselves and carry out their selfish desires. Those who protested were eliminated. These aggressive ones were misusing the items of sacred ceremonies, such as the sacred drink and sacred leaves which were smoked during inner vision quests. Sacred One told them that since addiction to sensation had taken over the majority of minds on the mainland, only a few were ready to gain the teachings that would help humanity progress in a positive way. Every person and family who he secretly asked to go with him had agreed wholeheartedly to do so. They knew that what Sacred One had said was true, and feared for their children, because whenever an aggressive one had too much of the ceremonial drink, they would either rape, kill, steal, or destroy.

Hummingbird loved the peace on the island Sacred One had chosen. The community of people truly helped each other and felt like one big family. She remembered the first time she saw SunWalker. He was much older than her, but she thought that some day, she wanted a mate just like him. He showed a kindness toward everything, and many men looked up to him.

Sacred One had caught Hummingbird following Sun-Walker around, while hiding behind the trees. "Come with me, little one," he said gently, as he took her hand and walked to a sunny meadow. After brushing off two large boulders, he pulled out some sweet berries and shared them with Hummingbird. "Tell me, little one," he began, "about your dreams. Your mother says that you are troubled by them."

"Not so much by them," Hummingbird responded, "but by what happens after them."

"What do you mean?" asked Sacred One.

"Sometimes I have a dream, and then learn from the women's talking circle that that was something which happened in the past before I was born. Then other times I will have a dream and it will happen in the future, just like I saw it. When they are scary, I do not like to have them...like when someone is going to die." She pouted and dropped her gaze to the ground.

"I see," hummed Sacred One. "Well, my little bird, you are not like other birds who can only fly forward. You, like the hummingbird, have a unique gift of being able to fly backward and forward. You can see into the past and into the future."

"But can I change the things I do not like," she interrupted.

"Sometimes," Sacred One began. "As you grow older, you will understand how to gain peace with some events just the way they are, for you will see how all is purposeful. Then, at other times, an inner knowing will show you what to do to prevent an imbalance from happening. But know this, little one, no matter what you do, all of life will eventually balance itself. This greater Truth will see you through any of the troubled times."

43

Hummingbird cherished her moments with Sacred One. He always knew how to lighten her heart, especially when she kept having scary dreams about the future.

"Tell me this, little one. What is the most important thing in your life, besides the Creator," asked Sacred One another day.

Hummingbird thought long and hard. "I suppose I should say my family. But the truth is: The People. All of the People feel like my family, so I would do anything for the good of the People."

"That is very wise for such a little one," Sacred One paused. "If you had a choice between your life being saved or the People being saved, which would you choose?"

"The People, of course," Hummingbird answered without hesitation.

"Are you sure?" Sacred One probed.

"Yes, what would I do alone without family and friends, and the fact that the People could continue to be, because of my sacrifice, would be the highest gift I could ever give."

"Who said anything about sacrifice?" inquired Sacred One.

"Oh!" Hummingbird clasped her hand over her mouth. "That is one of those stupid dreams I keep having...It's nothing," and off she ran before Sacred One could ask anything else; but he already knew her dream and the beauty of her soul.

STEADY TURTLE
one whose calm and simplicity
mask a greater knowing

Steady Turtle had shown strength and courage even as a little boy on the mainland of Mu. He volunteered to protect Sacred One, when he grew older, because he felt that Sacred One shared more than the others in the Brotherhood. After Sacred One taught Turtle how to meditate, Turtle could sense how some of the Brotherhood were hiding truths in order to have an advantage over the People. Steady Turtle's inner knowing had shown him how all people would gain by learning how to go within and become centered before making decisions or taking actions which could have repercussions. Since Turtle seemed to take longer than most people when making decisions or taking actions, he gained the reputation of being slow and steady, like the turtle in the story about the race between the hare and the turtle. However, his slow and steady ways usually proved to be the best path.

Each of the families had guards or helpers on the island where Sacred One had taken the people. In this way, all the single people felt connected with a family, and it strengthened the community as a whole. "Seeing how we can serve each other, keeps us focused on WE rather than ME," Sacred One would say. "Share all you do as though the Creator is doing it through you. Think before you talk or communicate, and ask if the Creator would say those words."

Turtle had come to love his adopted family, and felt as though Many Stars were his own Grandmother, often calling her that. Many Stars also felt deeply connected with Turtle, and found that she could rely on his steady pace. Turtle took good care of Many Stars on their journey following Sun-Walker. They were only a day's journey away from the village when Turtle spied Raven and a group of men at a morning campsite. He overheard their conversation.

"We did not have time to wait for Feathered Trumpet to recover from his head injury," Raven argued. "Those who took the Sacred Feathers were escaping. Feathered Trumpet will be glad when we bring them back to him."

So Raven is finally beginning to take over, mused Turtle. He had sensed her desire to use and then discard the cocky Feathered Trumpet when the time was right; but how was Turtle going to travel in the same direction as this hunting party, while keeping Many Stars hidden and safe.

Just then, one of the guards returned to the campsite pulling Many Stars along with him. "Oh, Grandmother," Turtle sighed, "I asked you not to sing your morning prayers out loud. Why did you not listen?"

"The tones of the prayer need to be heard and felt by the body," he remembered her response.

"I guess the only thing to do now is surrender also, and act like a dumb and unknowing servant," thought Steady Turtle. "Perhaps I can cleverly lead them off the trail of SunWalker and Keymyu, until I figure out a way to escape."

So, after gathering his belongings at their hiding place, Turtle meekly approached Raven's band, with a hunched over back, and he continually dropped their supplies like a feeble-minded person. He told Many Stars in her thoughts what he was planning to do. She smirked at him, and then quickly looked down at the ground trying to compose herself.

HAWK
one who can soar above to see the broader picture

Hawk had joyfully reunited with Moonbeam and the community on the beach. He was grateful that Hummingbird had the inner vision to prepare for a long journey. They were well on their way when Hummingbird suddenly said, "Stop! We need to go in this direction."

"That is the old path we took, Hummingbird. I am trying to create another path as a diversion," responded Hawk.

"But someone precious is in danger, and we need to help," insisted Hummingbird. "Can you take just a few moments and use your bird's eye perception to see if I am right?"

Her tone was so insistent that Hawk agreed, and went off on his own to use his inner journeying skills (which SunWalker had taught him), and soar over the area to see what was ahead on the path he had taken before with SunWalker. After centering himself, he retraced the path as he remembered it, from a hawk's perspective. There below, near the ravine where SunWalker had hit his head, was a dark haired woman and band of men, tying up a very old woman and her meek companion. "Could this be SunWalker's mother?" he wondered. "Laughing Wolf had said that Steady Turtle would be following them, but could that cowardly person be Steady Turtle?"

Hawk soared higher, surveying the path ahead to see where he could create a trap. He found the perfect place, and then returned to Hummingbird and his group.

"Yes, I think I see what you were sensing," Hawk admitted to Hummingbird. "It will take us out of our way, but if that is SunWalker's mother, then she definitely needs our help."

47

Hummingbird smiled. She had been doing her own journeying, and shared some added information of how to set the trap. Hawk was grateful at her advice on the motivation of their adversary. It gave him the bait to pull them into the trap.

Raven was getting tired of the clumsy companion to the older woman. He kept slowing them down. "Maybe I should get rid of him," she thought out loud. "It is just the old woman who is important. She is related to that young girl taken with the Sacred Feathers. Maybe I can create an exchange: the old woman's life for the Feathers."

A child's high shrill caught her off guard. She quickly crouched down and moved through the bushes toward the sound. "Look mother," the child shrieked, "Some special feathers are lodged in this tree. Someone walking on the cliff above must have dropped them, and they fell way down here. They look very old. Look at these knots tied in the leather casing."

Could it be that this child has found the Sacred Feathers? Raven's heart accelerated, but then her clever mind sensed a trap. "This is much too easy," she thought. She circled back to her group and sent two men out to search the area for any sign of other people. The rest of the group hid in the area surrounding the boy and his mother, making sure that they could not escape. Once Raven felt that the area was safe, and no other people were around to interfere, she would approach the boy and his mother.

Hawk and enough men to out-number Raven's group were carefully hidden in a cave next to the boy and his mother. The only way for anyone to find them, would have been to search the area near the boy and woman. However, Hawk knew that the best strategy for Raven was to search the surrounding area without being seen, and then surprise the boy and woman before they could get away. He made sure to have his men add extra shrubs at the cave entrance, to camouflage it completely.

When Raven and her men finally approached the boy and his mother, mentioning how she had dropped some special feathers while walking on the cliff, Steady Turtle sensed that something unusual was about to happen. There was no way SunWalker or Keymyu would have dropped the Feathers, and then left them behind. He motioned for Many Stars to stay near a boulder and hide behind it if fighting began. In this way, she would not be used for ransom by Raven's group.

No sooner had he finished his thoughts, than Hawk's men sprang out from the cave and completely surprised Raven's group. They tied Raven and her men, and took all their weapons and supplies. Hopefully, if Raven did happen to get loose, she would be more likely to return back to the village than continue her search without weapons or food.

Steady Turtle introduced himself while helping tie up Raven and her men. "So you are not as feeble as you pretend to be," smiled Hawk, and the two men had a good laugh together.

Many Stars knew that it was safe now to come out from behind the boulder, but a group of people standing up on the cliff caught her attention. She could not help staring at the young woman with reddish hair. It seemed like Sparkling Water was standing right beside her, but in light form. When Hawk explained how he was part of the community which lived with SunWalker on the beach, Many Stars began to fit the pieces together. Sparkling Water must be helping us find each other, she decided, and gladly joined the group as it traveled eastward toward SunWalker and her granddaughter Keymyu. She learned that the red headed woman was called Hummingbird.

Four days and nights had passed as Raven persisted in trying to free herself. All the others in her group had died from starvation or the cold of night. She grimaced as she used their dead bodies to keep herself warm at night; but her will was

49

strong, and she finally got her feet free. Thus with hands still bound behind her back and weak from hunger, Raven slowly made her way back to the village. The winds and rain probably washed all traces of the trail that group made, she reasoned. Her only hope of survival was to return to the village. She must get those Sacred Feathers because her power and destiny were linked with them. This persistent thought gave her strength enough to return home. Only time would tell how she could one day retrieve those Feathers.

LAUGHING WOLF
one whose light heart brings joy to others

Hummingbird had been right about the journey being very long. As each month of her pregnancy passed, she became weaker and weaker. Keymyu and Many Stars stayed close by her, using all the healing remedies they could find in this new land. However, one morning during her eighth month, as Hummingbird attempted to get up from her blanket, her legs gave out from underneath her. Fortunately, Keymyu was close enough to catch Hummingbird before she fell and hurt herself; and Many Stars ran over quickly to help ease Hummingbird back down on to her blanket.

In frustration, Hummingbird cried that she did not want to hold the group up. "We feel so close to where our new homeland will be," she sighed.

"I have been feeling the same way," said Keymyu. "Every time we come to another opening in the trees, I wonder if this is it. And then something seems to say NO."

"Have you noticed how there seems to be a gray wolf at each clearing?" commented Many Stars. "I must be seeing things, but it looks like it is the same wolf, each time."

Hummingbird smiled, "It is the same wolf. And perhaps you did not notice, but a crow is usually somewhere nearby."

"I did notice," laughed Keymyu, "and whichever way the crow flies, the wolf seems to follow."

Laughing Wolf could not help over-hearing this conversation, since he was close by, while repairing his tools. He did not know anything about a crow or a wolf, but he did know that it would be unwise for Hummingbird to walk any further. Thus, after gathering Steady Turtle, they went off into a wooded area, and by mid-day, they returned with something which could be used to carry Hummingbird. Wolf and Turtle demonstrated how the branches could rest on two men's shoulders, while the area woven with twigs in the center, could be used to lie on, or sit on. "A blanket will soften the center area," Wolf added.

Tears welled up in Hummingbird's eyes. How often Wolf would create something to ease another's burden. She pulled out two crow feathers from her medicine bag, and handed one to Wolf and the other to Turtle. "The shells sewn on them are from our homeland, Mu," she explained. "Sacred One had given me a handful of shells when I was a little girl. He told me that whenever I needed help, I was to pull out one of these shells, and offer it to Great Sprit with a prayer. I have been collecting the crow feathers for my son, and sewing a shell on each feather as I found it. But since you have helped my son (and his weary mother) on this journey, I know he would gladly share two of his feathers with the two of you. Thank you, I would not have been able to continue without this...this...what shall we call it?"

"Your sacred seat, oh wise one," bowed Laughing Wolf with great style, and everyone who had gathered around them laughed, and then bowed in the same manner. Hummingbird blushed and giggled along with them, and bowed back, while still sitting on her blanket.

The "sacred seat" became the focal point for much laughter, which eased the weariness of everyone on this journey. One evening, for example, Wolf served an entire meal to everyone, carrying the meal on the "sacred seat" with Turtle's help. Another evening Moonbeam and Keymyu made up a humorous dance using the "sacred seat." And Turtle, who was quite a story teller, invented a humorous story of how the "sacred seat" had first begun in ancient times. All of this humor helped draw attention away from Hummingbird needing special care, which would have made her feel awkward and embarrassed. She thanked and blessed Wolf many times in her prayers. "You are a loyal and treasured friend to everyone," she thought. "Somehow you combine the cleverness of a wolf and the laughter of a joyful heart. No wonder you are called Laughing Wolf."

It had been easy for Keymyu to accept Hummingbird as SunWalker's new companion and mate, since Hummingbird reminded her so much of Sparkling Water. Often, as Hummingbird spoke, it sounded just like what Sparkling Water would have said. As well, Hummingbird shared with Keymyu, how much she had admired SunWalker and Sparkling Water as a couple. "They balanced each other, showed respect for each other, and were willing to listen and learn from each other," she explained.

Hummingbird also told Keymyu how she and Sun-Walker were just friends for a long time. "We were meditating together one day," she shared, "when both of us experienced the feeling that I would one day carry SunWalker's child. Both of us were too embarrassed to talk about it, at first, since we were just friends at that point. But, as each day passed, we grew closer and closer, until one day we knew it was time to join together in a ceremony as lifetime companions."

"SunWalker had shared with me how much he wanted to find you and his mother," she continued. "So, when he had a vision to go to Feathered Trumpet's new ceremony to look for you both, I understood, and encouraged him to follow his inner guidance."

By now, everyone on the journey had heard the story of how SunWalker and Keymyu were brother and sister, rather than father and daughter. After SunWalker carefully guided the People through Sacred One's life and difficult choices, all accepted what had happened, and they were ready to bring new and more healthy choices into their future. That was why they were so eager to learn the wisdom from the Ancient Ones.

Evenings by the fire had become special for the People in this new land. Keymyu was asked to share the teachings she had learned on her voyage across the Great Waters, and SunWalker was asked to share the skills of meditation which Sacred One had taught him.

THE ANCIENT ONES
those who saw the Creator in everything

One evening as the stars glistened, and the People's hunger had been satisfied by a light, but nourishing meal, Keymyu began to share what she had learned from the Ancient Ones.

"The Ancients began by explaining the essence of life," she shared. "There are many stories with symbols of webs and spirals, and all of this is valid. But let me tell you the straight forward way in which the Ancients presented it to me. First, let's take a few moments to come to a meditative state, before I begin," she suggested, and then paused to allow everyone to become peaceful.

Keymyu was going to start with the words "in the beginning," but remembered that the Ancients referred to this as "the Unknown," so began like this. "In the Unknown, the ALL (or Divine Unity) created vibration and particle (or energy and form) (that which is unseen and that which is seen). The ALL changed from just being, into exploring beingness and all its possibilities." She paused to let these new concepts sink in.

"The seed of possibility was within the void," she continued. "And a disordered movement, seeking to extend itself, was upon the face of the deep."

"The Spirit of Life (or the Breath of Life) moved within the womb of the Universe. And the Being of Beings called energy and form into action." After another long pause, she continued. "The ALL saw that the Light (or its regenerative power) would continue to balance itself within Itself."

"Then the Divine Unity separated the light (or expanding regenerating energy) from darkness (or contracting degenerating energy). This is like separating the process of breathing

55

out-from breathing in," she explained. "They are both part of one breath, but can also be seen as separate experiences. Within all of Life, there is that which generates, that which de-generates, and that which re-generates again. This is how Life continues to be, and to understand these three forces-is to understand the essence of life. The Creator does not judge any aspect of life, but sees all as purposeful in the on-going balance of energy within Life.

"For example, if part of the forest did not degenerate, we would have no place to walk," she joked, and the ones who were following her, chuckled. However, Keymyu could see that the way the Ancients had explained it to her, was a bit abstract for most of the People. So she had to repeat the ideas many times and in many different ways.

"All that the Creator made was good," Keymyu continued another evening. "And the concept of good means 'balanced' to the Ancients. Humans were supposed to be part of the balance in life, but they began to think separately from the Creator, and thus began to do things differently from the way the Creator had originally intended."

"The law of Giving and Receiving is part of the Law of Balance," Keymyu continued. "For example, the air that we breathe out, is the air which plants take in; and then the plants transform the air into that which is good for us to breathe in again. If we take care of the plants and trees, and all that Mother Earth provides for us, we will be in balance with the law of Giving and Receiving. But if we destroy too many plants, trees, and creatures of the Earth, then we will destroy the balance, and eventually ourselves. That is why caring for the Earth, and the environment around us, is one of the important jobs we have as human beings."

"The law of Giving and Receiving also brings balance in human relationships. If one person takes too much, for

56

example, the other person (who gives all the time) will become depleted, or exhausted, and eventually stop giving, and the relationship will die. Two givers create the best relationship, if they also know how to receive, and then give again to keep the cycle going."

"Here is another example," expounded Keymyu. "A balanced person would not visit a friend's dwelling and expect that friend to provide shelter, food, and so forth without giving something in return. A balanced person would make sure to bring food to share, and would help in useful ways. A taker, on the other hand, would be looking for how much they could get for free, without having to share anything in return."

"On the mainland of Mu, the majority of people had forgotten the ancient law of Giving and Receiving. Some aggressive ones were hoarding supplies, and thus created a lack for others. This allowed the aggressive ones to manipulate the others by making the others work for them, in order to get food for their families."

"How many of you can remember a time when we shared what we had so that everyone in the community was taken care of, and everyone did their fair share of the work?" Keymyu asked. Only a handful of people could remember when the People thought in terms of WE rather than ME. Keymyu suddenly realized that there was a great deal of un-learning to do, before the new understanding could begin.

To help review the essence of life, Keymyu began a different way on another evening. "Before that which is called 'the Beginning,' the Divine Unity encompassed ALL. Being ALL, that which is called male or female, was united, and experienced as One, rather than as separate aspects."

"The realm of separate seeing allows the ALL to experience diversity and all that it can become," she continued. "The human mind allows the One to experience the uniqueness of each of its aspects."

57

Keymyu closed her eyes to feel the rest as she spoke. "To return to the ALL, the Oneness, is a sacred experience. In those precious moments, one feels united with all of life. All judgments and grievances are suspended. They do not exist in Oneness."

"From the viewpoint of the ALL, every color of skin is like a different hue of the rainbow; every way of praising the Infinite is like the many melodies of the songbirds; every lesson in life's journey is like another bend in the Great River."

"Who are we to judge the rainbow, the songbirds, or the river's flow. We are but a traveler on the journey of infinite possibilities. And we are the journey and the infinite possibilities, as well."

Life is ALL. We are a part of the ALL. And, in sacred moments, we are at One with the ALL."

When Keymyu opened her eyes and looked out at the People, she saw rainbows of color above them. They finally understand, she celebrated, and allowed them to meditate on these words in silence.

SunWalker shared with the People on another occasion. "Each morning, greet the rising sun with gratitude; and each evening, say a blessing toward the setting sun. Before sleeping, review the day and see what lessons you have learned, and thank your teachers. Send blessings and healing energy to everyone and everything in life. Bask in the Love of the Creative Spirit, and send it forth to help other people open their hearts, minds and souls to the Creative Energy of Divine Love."

"A morning and an evening prayer will change the energy and experience of your life," he continued. "Rather than give you words to memorize, allow the sincerity of your heart to speak. The Creative Force of the Universe responds to the INTENTION of your thoughts, words and actions. What you give out...is what you will receive."

"Let us meditate and commune as One together, and then I will say a prayer that Sacred One shared with me. We will remain silent for a while after I share the prayer." Sun-Walker prayed out loud:

"Our Father-Mother, the Breath of Life in All.
As I call Your Name, my heart opens.
Your Wisdom is ever present within me.
And as I follow your Inner Guidance,
        each moment unfolds.
Thank you for providing what I need for today,
        in this present moment.
And thank you for releasing the ties that bind
        me to the past;
For as I allow my heart to return to the state
        of innocence (as You created me), I will
        see Your Beauty and Joy in everything.
Continue to lead me back to Your Strength
        and Wisdom, so fear will not cause me
        to make mistakes.
For all is a part of Your Life, and Your Power,
        and Your Glory, as Life continues on and on."

The hearts and the souls of the People united with this prayer, and they asked SunWalker to say it again, so they could repeat it after him. As the People opened more and more to the Infinite, the Ancient Ones were able to touch their hearts so that more love, kindness and balance radiated in everything they shared together. The People became more aware of how to discern between the fear of the human ego, and the peace which comes from inner knowing.

One morning as the People reached the top of a ridge, they all seemed to sigh at once when a golden eagle soared above them. "This is the place!" whispered Keymyu to

59

SunWalker in one ear, while Hummingbird was whispering the same thing in his other ear. He burst out laughing and hugged them both.

"Yes, I know," he agreed, and before he could say anything to the People, they also knew. Many began racing down to the valley below, which seemed to glimmer in the morning light.

"I need to sit," proclaimed Hummingbird, in pain; but everyone around her was already heading down to the valley. "Great Spirit, help me," she cried as her birthing pain increased. "Everyone has gone down the mountain, and I am here alone with my son on his way. Help me, please."

Keymyu felt the wings of a bird whisk the back of her head, as it flew closer than a bird would normally fly; and Many Stars stopped dead in her tracks when a gray wolf suddenly appeared in the middle of the path. Keymyu also saw the wolf and stopped.

The crow then whisked against Many Stars' cheek and began flying back up the path they had taken. The wolf made a quick "yelp" and then followed the crow. Keymyu and Many Stars caught each other's eyes. "Hummingbird!" they both thought together.

Keymyu grabbed some of the women, and quickly raced back up the mountain in search of Hummingbird. Many Stars knew that it would be difficult for her to race up the mountain, so asked some women to follow Keymyu and take the birthing supplies she had been carrying.

Hummingbird had almost gone unconscious by the time Keymyu reached her. Her son must have been anxious to face the new world, because fortunately, the birthing process was fast, and the group of women arrived just in time to help.

The eagle, which was seen earlier, continued to circle directly above the birthing. When the newborn arrived, the eagle screeched, the crow squawked, and the wolf howled (which was unusual, since this was daytime, not nighttime).

All the women looked at each other in awe. Then Grandfather Wind sang through the pine trees above them, and all sorts of sounds of greeting came from the surrounding forest.

"The creatures of Earth are glad that you are finally here, CrowWolf," Hummingbird said to her son in her thoughts. "They have been waiting for you to come and help us all get back in balance with the Creator's sacred ways." She snuggled the baby in her arms. "You will always have a crow and a wolf to help you, as they have been helping me. Learn from them, my son. They will share the wisdom of the ancient ways."

Wolf and Turtle used the "sacred seat" again to carry the new mother and her child down to the valley of glimmering light. Two celebrations took place that evening: one for their new home, and the other for the new member of their community. Keymyu shared how the eagle screeched, the crow squawked, and the wolf howled at the birth of their new member. "Then Grandfather Wind sang through the tall pines, as other creatures in the forest shared greetings to the newborn," she explained. Everyone felt chills of excitement while hearing the story of the birth. Later, all passed by Hummingbird, SunWalker and their new son, giving them blessings and feeling the awe and power of this special occasion.

The Naming Ceremony came soon, since SunWalker already knew that Hummingbird wanted to call their son "CrowWolf." He was in agreement since he had watched how a crow and wolf had been following them (or leading them) ever since Hummingbird was first with child.

"Thank you, Great Spirit, Creator, all our Ancestors and Ancient Ones who have been guiding us and protecting us. May our new life in this new place reflect your Wisdom and Sacred Ways," prayed SunWalker, not only that evening, but every evening for a full cycle of the moon.

THE SACRED FEATHERS
what you give...you receive

By the time Raven had returned to her village, the people had run out of the liquid she provided for them to drink at every meal. Without this drink to dull their minds, they began to see what kind of a leader Feathered Trumpet really was: selfish and arrogant.

"How long are we going to tolerate him?" many began to ask. "And Raven is just as bad," others responded. "Let's get rid of both of them!" A wave of protest began to circulate throughout the village.

At the edge of the village, Raven heard these cries of protest, and thus decided to sneak back to her dwelling without being seen. Her servants helped her undo the ropes around her wrists, and then bathed her and brought her food. "How is Feathered Trumpet doing?" she inquired.

"His head injury healed, but he seems to be more stormy than ever, especially with all the talk about getting rid of him," replied one of her servants.

The village had grown very large. Most of the people who had traveled long distances to see the new ceremony, had decided to stay. However, the increase of people caused food shortages; therefore, fights broke out regularly. Feathered Trumpet had enough guards to control a small village, but the number of people in the village now greatly outnumbered his guards and weapons. He could no longer control the people with brute strength and empty promises.

"Those Feathers were my only hope to keep control," Feathered Trumpet grumbled as he paced back and forth, looking out at the mass hysteria brewing below his fortified dwelling, now at the top of the Great Mound.

A servant brought him news that Raven had returned without her men and without the Sacred Feathers. "Maybe I should sacrifice her to the people," he raged. "That might keep their feeble minds occupied while I escape."

However, when Feathered Trumpet stormed into Raven's dwelling, and had his guards seize her, she calmly responded, "Once I am gone, then what? The people will still be angry. Your only hope is to reclaim the Sacred Feathers. And I am the only one who knows which way the group, who took them, went." She had planned her strategy while returning home. "So if you destroy me, then you destroy all hope of getting the Feathers and maintaining control over the people. Let me have a group of guards and supplies, and I will find the Feathers and bring them back," Raven concluded.

"What kind of a fool do you think I am?" Feathered Trumpet scoffed. "You would take those feathers and keep on going. No, if a group is going to retrieve the Feathers, then I am going with them, to make sure I get them in the end."

"Do as you wish," Raven conceded. "But remember that you need me to find them. I heard where that group was heading," she lied, "and know how to get there."

Feathered Trumpet eyed her suspiciously, but what other choice did he have. He had no clue how to find the group who took the Feathers, and the crowds were becoming more rebellious every moment. He turned to a guard at his right. "Create a figure that looks like me, wearing my Feathered Headdress," Trumpet ordered. "Have the figure sitting in view of those below the Great Mound." Then, turning to the guards to his left, he ordered, "Gather as many supplies and weapons as you can. We need to leave right away."

Raven hid her smile, but Trumpet turned her around and said, "You better pack for a long journey, Raven. And I would not want to be you if we do not find the people with the

Sacred Feathers." He frowned at her with venom in his eyes.

Before long, Raven, Feathered Trumpet and all his guards were on their way retracing the path Raven had taken on her return home. As they prepared their campsite on the first night, Feathered Trumpet asked Raven, "Why do those Feathers have so much power?"

She replied, "Sacred One used to say that it was not so much the Feathers, which had power, but the one who used them."

Feathered Trumpet frowned at what he considered another attempt by Raven to show him that he needed her to control the people. However Raven had heard Sacred One say those very words, and was hoping they were not completely accurate. "What if the Feathers only respond to the rightful heir?" she questioned in her mind. Then her quest for them would be in vain. "NO, that cannot be," she decided. "Why would I have had that vision of leading the people with Feathers in my hand? The vision was so real...it has to be true," she concluded.

As the moons passed, Raven used all her powers of persuasion and magic to convince Feathered Trumpet she was going in the right direction. She pointed to birds flying in a certain direction - as a sign; branches broken in a certain way - as a sign; lightning flashing in the distance - as a sign. All that time, she kept hoping that she was correct. Before she was captured and tied up by those people with the Feathers, they seemed to be traveling toward the rising sun. She hoped they had continued in the same direction.

In the valley of glimmering light, Keymyu decided to follow the idea in her morning meditation. She asked Hummingbird if she could take care of CrowWolf that morning, and brought him to the cave where SunWalker had shown her the stones which glistened in the sunlight. SunWalker called them crystals, and showed Keymyu how they gave off a pulsing energy when one held them.

CrowWolf cooed and smiled when Keymyu placed him gently on the bed of crystals, with two blankets underneath to protect him from any sharp edges. The morning meditation had also brought forth the image of the Sacred Feathers, so Keymyu brought them as well. As she put her hand on CrowWolf's heart, the thought came to place the Sacred Feathers on CrowWolf.

Carefully, Keymyu placed the Feathers on the baby so that the tips pointed toward his head. A powerful energy began to surge from the baby and Feathers. Keymyu felt chills prickling her skin. She closed her eyes and sensed images of ancient people communicating with birds and animals. Then she saw CrowWolf going on a long journey with a crow and a wolf leading him. "This child is very powerful," she thought as she carried him back to his mother.

As CrowWolf grew older, Keymyu noticed how birds, animals, spiders, snakes, and all sorts of creatures, were drawn to him. She also noticed that whenever the Sacred Feathers were used in a ceremony, the young boy would turn the palm of his hands in their direction. She wondered if he was feeling their energy, or adding his own energy to the Feathers.

🖋 🖋 🖋 🖋

Giant Feathers swooped down from the sky and attacked Feathered Trumpet in his dreams. He shook himself awake in a cold sweat, and held his hand on his forehead. "Why do these headaches and bad dreams keep happening?" he wondered.

Raven watched out of the corner of her eye with her sleeping blanket almost covering her face. The leaves she had slipped into Trumpet's drink last night were helping his behavior become more erratic. Each day she watched how the guards became more and more wary of him. At just the right moment, she would win the guards over, and leave Feathered Trumpet by himself in the jungle.

She had not told anyone that she had seen smoke the day before, in the distance to the North. This gave her a new direction to head, but she wanted to get rid of Trumpet before they reached the place where she saw the smoke. She estimated that it was about a two days' journey away.

With the morning breakfast, Raven added more of the finely ground leaves to Trumpet's meal. She had discovered these leaves near their old village. When tasting a tiny piece of one, she realized that they caused hallucinations in the mind. She wondered what eating a greater amount of them would do. So, she dried the leaves and carefully marked them in her medicine bundle with an unusual knot.

As Feathered Trumpet finished his meal, he groaned and then swung his fists at one of the guards for no apparent reason. Then, when Trumpet took out a large knife and was about to slay the guard, the guard's friend tripped Feathered Trumpet, and tied his hands.

"He is unconscious. What do we do now?" The guard asked, and everyone looked at Raven.

"Give him this to calm him," she said, as she handed one of the guards a potion which she knew would put Trumpet to sleep for a long time. She wanted to make sure Trumpet did not hear how she was going to convince the guards to follow her.

Within minutes, Feathered Trumpet was snoring, and Raven began her persuasion. "Ever since that head injury," she began, "he has been unpredictable. I am not surprised he tried to attack one of his own men. He has been having strange dreams at night, and then was still reacting to them when awake. I think his mind is going. We can leave him here with someone to watch him," she continued, "and I will resume the

67

trip. I saw some smoke about a two days' journey away, so it won't be long before we can get the Feathers and return home."

No one wanted to stay with Feathered Trumpet (which did not surprise Raven), but she made it their decision to leave him alone. In this way, she could say she was not responsible for what happened to him. If she could get the men to leave right now, she thought, that would give her at least a half a day's journey before Feathered Trumpet awoke.

Before Raven spoke her thoughts about leaving, one of the guards remarked, "The sooner we get those Feathers, the sooner we can go home. So let's get going toward the smoke you saw, Raven."

"Great," she thought, "my plan is working." Raven and the guards headed North, leaving Feathered Trumpet slumped against a tree with his hands tied in front of him and his large knife in his lap.

It was closer to a three days' journey before Raven's group arrived at the place where the smoke had been. They crouched behind some bushes and watched a group of people near a large fire. An elderly woman was holding a child in her arms, while another woman was feeding the child some liquid. Raven sensed that the child was sick, and wondered where all the men were. There were mostly women and children in this group, with only two young men that she could see.

This did not look like the group of people who had tied her up at the ravine; but the woman holding the child looked familiar. "Was this someone from the mainland of Mu?" she wondered.

Raven told the men to stay in their hiding place. Since she was a woman, this group would probably not feel threatened by her. She would find out where the men were. Slowly and peacefully, Raven approached the group with her palms up, showing that she was not carrying a weapon. The woman holding the child gasped in surprise when she recognized the healer from Mu who had healed her leg from a poisonous snake bite.

"Praise be to the Creator," cried the old woman as she moved toward Raven. "You have come to heal my son as you healed my leg long ago. Help us, please, before we all die from the sickness of the bad water."

While Raven examined the child's tongue, eyes and pulse, the old woman explained how their men drank bad water on their last hunting trip. One man managed to return home, but whatever had killed the other men soon killed him, and then spread to other members of the community. Raven also learned that these people left Feathered Trumpet's village as soon as he declared himself leader. They saw immediately how he would be a selfish and arrogant leader, and they decided to risk the jungle before surrendering to his ruthlessness.

Raven finally realized that this was not the group who took the Sacred Feathers. She asked them if they had met or seen any other groups on their journey. The old woman told her that there was a group to the South, some people in the Northeast, and still others toward the Southeast.

Raven felt exhausted just thinking of all the traveling she would have to do to check out all those communities. But then, the child she had given the herbs to, suddenly opened his eyes; and before she knew what was happening, the people were preparing a feast for her and asking her to stay as their Medicine Woman. Raven felt it was safe now to tell these people that she was traveling with a group of men. She decided to tell them that they were on a sacred journey.

The community of mostly women were excited to invite Raven's men to their feast. "Perhaps we can rest here a while," Raven thought. "The men will renew their spirits with all the attention from these eager women." So she continued ministering herbs to the sick ones, and enjoyed the feast and merriment that evening. Little did she know that the guards would become attached to this place and refuse to leave for many cycles of the seasons.

🖋 🖋 🖋 🖋

When Feathered Trumpet opened his eyes, everything around him seemed blurry. At first he thought that he was back in the old village, but then his mind slowly remembered how he was on a journey to recover the Sacred Feathers.

"Guards," he yelled out, as his weakened legs buckled when he tried to stand up. A clinking noise of something falling made him realize that his hands were tied in front of him, and he had just dropped his large knife. "What?" he scoffed in disbelief, "Who would have tied me up like this?" Vague memories of swinging at a guard and then being tripped, came back to him. "They would not leave me here like this...unless...unless Raven talked them into it!" he proclaimed. "I should have known to watch her more carefully."

It did not take long for Feathered Trumpet to move the twine around his wrist back and forth against his large knife, until he was free. But which way did they go? He was not sure. Since they had been heading East most of the time, he decided to follow the natural break in the undergrowth that headed slightly Southeast. "Wait until I find her," he grumbled over and over, while hacking the undergrowth out of his way. "Wait until I find her!"

After five days of eating and drinking whatever he could find, Feathered Trumpet was beginning to feel that he was lost. He squatted by a small stream to cup some water with his hands and gather his thoughts. Suddenly, splashing and yelling sounds came from down the stream. Trumpet jumped back quickly so he could observe what was happening without being seen.

70

Two young boys were fighting furiously. "If you hadn't dropped that log at the ravine, we could have gotten back across. Now we're trapped on this side and can't get home," yelled one boy. "But the log cracked, and that giant beast was after us." screamed the other boy. "It was about to come across the log and get us." The two kept hitting and punching and splashing, until they were both so exhausted that they sat down in the water, panting for breath.

As Feathered Trumpet carefully approached them, he searched the area around where they had entered the stream. The pair of footprints assured him that these two boys were alone. Their language was very much like his. If he could help them find their way home, maybe he would be rewarded for his efforts, he schemed. "Perhaps I can help you two," began Feathered Trumpet as he approached the boys.

Startled, the boys began scrambling to their feet to run away from this large unknown man with unkempt hair and filthy body. But Trumpet yelled out quickly, "Better not go that way. I saw the giant beast over there."

The boys froze immediately, looked at each other, then at the strange man, then at each other again. "The one that is brownish yellow with black spots?" asked the shorter boy.

"Yes," smiled Trumpet. "It was ferocious." He sounded the last word in a roaring manner.

"Who are you?" inquired the taller boy, wanting more information before he chose to trust this stranger over another encounter with the beast.

"I am..." Feathered Trumpet stalled a minute, while trying to come up with a believable tale. "I am Brave One, the one who travels the jungles to make sure children are not eaten by beasts." When the boys gave each other a skeptical glance, Trumpet altered his story a bit. "I am actually on a vision quest for a sacred journey. It is a secret, and I was not supposed to tell anyone until I found the stolen sacred object. But seeing the beast so close to you boys, I could not live knowing that I had allowed it to eat you."

That got the boys' attention. The beast was close by? They huddled closer together. Trumpet saw that this approach was working better. "Do either of you know how to swing a knife like this?" He held up his large knife so the sun's reflection on it would make it seem even more ominous.

"I..I..I do," stuttered the taller boy, trying to be brave.

"Then, here," Trumpet said, handing him the large knife. "You guard us for a moment while I wash my face and body to become presentable for your people. Do you live far away?" he added while splashing his face.

"No," responded the boy holding the knife and surveying the area for danger. "Once we get back over the ravine, we know our way home. It's not far."

"But to be safe, you will need me and my sacred knife to protect you," boasted Trumpet. He decided that his sacred journey also needed a sacred knife to embellish the story.

The two boys looked at each other. It did not take long for them to decide that traveling home with this stranger would be safer than traveling home alone. So when Feathered Trumpet was washed and presentable, he had the boys show him where the ravine was.

The crevice in the earth was wider and deeper than Trumpet had imagined. He looked in both directions to see if they could cross at a better place. The canyon looked as though it went as far as the eyes could see, and the drop was too steep to climb. The only way across would be to find or build something long enough to walk across.

"You said that there was a log long enough to get across here?" Trumpet asked in disbelief.

"Yes, it had fallen from the other side and just reached to this side. We were both frightened to run across it, but the beast was right behind us," explained the taller boy.

"And the log cracked when I came after him," added the other boy. "Then when I went to lift it and shake it, so the beast would not follow us across, the log broke and fell down to the bottom." They all looked over the edge, but could not see any trace of the log.

"I am going to have to build something safe to cross this large crevice," Feathered Trumpet decided, and began instructing the boys what to gather. It took almost two days to cut and tie logs and twigs together to make a safe bridge. All three of them were needed to carefully lift and then angle the wooden structure so it safely rested on the other side. Trumpet carefully tested it before he allowed the boys to cross it.

By the time the boys and their new friend had arrived home, they had all sorts of stories to tell their people about how brave and resourceful this man was. The name "Brave One" stuck, and Trumpet like that better than Feathered Trumpet. It felt good to be honored and admired by people again. Maybe he should stay in this place for a while. Their leader was very old. Perhaps they would need a new leader very soon, he reasoned. Meanwhile, he was asked to train the boys in hunting and building skills. These were a simple people, and thus he appeared to be someone with great abilities in their eyes.

🖋 🖋 🖋 🖋

When twelve full cycles of the seasons had passed, CrowWolf was as skilled a hunter as men twice his age. He often hunted alone because he liked to commune with the animal before he met it in the wild; and then he made sure to thank it for presenting itself as food for the People. He carefully used every aspect of the animal for tools, weapons, carrying containers, clothes, or gifts, so nothing was wasted.

CrowWolf's mother had taught him to honor every part of Mother Earth as sacred. Hummingbird told him, "Treat everyone and everything with kindness. Move through the day with joy and gratitude for all the Creator has provided...all the beauty for your eyes to see...all the sounds for your ears to hear...all the tastes for your mouth to enjoy. Listen to everything as though the Creator is speaking to you through it. Allow humility to keep your heart open. Pride will shut the door to knowing the truth."

Hummingbird watched as her son sharpened his tools. He often sat somewhere near the Sacred Feathers. She wondered if he communed with them, or just liked being near their energy.

A hawk circling above caught her attention as she began hiking toward the place where she usually meditated in the morning. After becoming still with her eyes closed, she focused on a point in the center area of her forehead. Peace filled her and continued until a hawk's cry caused her to open her eyes. The hawk flying overhead dropped something like a stick, which plopped on the ground behind a bush nearby. "That is unusual," thought Hummingbird. Curiosity caused her to go and look at what was dropped. There was a stick on the ground behind the bush, but there were also four hawk feathers. "They have the same shape and size as the Sacred Feathers," she mused. "Since CrowWolf is so fond of the Sacred Feathers, I think I will make him a holder and carrying case for these hawk feathers. I will design it like the one which holds the Sacred Feathers. Then he will have his own 'sacred feathers,'" she smiled.

When Hummingbird finished her gift and presented it to CrowWolf, his eyes sparkled with delight. "Mother!" he gasped. "I just had a dream last night in which a hawk presented me with something, but I could not see what it was. I will show this to our friend, Hawk, and ask him if he will help me learn how to soar above and see the broader picture."

"These feathers are just for you, CrowWolf," Hummingbird responded. "You are a very generous person, so I do not want you to give them away. It is important that you keep them." As she said this last sentence, she knew somehow that it was true, but did not know why.

CrowWolf showed the new hawk feathers to his friends and family, and made sure to carry them with him wherever he went. Hawk gladly showed CrowWolf the skill of soaring above to see the broader picture. CrowWolf thanked him by giving Hawk one of the many crow feathers with a shell sewn on it that his mother had made for him. Hawk had always admired the crow feathers that both Wolf and Turtle had. He remembered Wolf remarking how he felt his skin prickle with energy when Hummingbird handed the crow feather to him. Hawk felt the same prickly sensation when CrowWolf handed the crow feather to him. "I will honor this feather and shell from Mu as much as you honor your hawk feathers," Hawk said with reverence.

"And I will honor you, my good friend Hawk. May you and Moonbeam be blessed with the child you want," Crow-Wolf said as his eyes lowered to the ground and he began walking away. Then he turned to add, "You may want to have Moonbeam tie the crow feather in her hair."

Hawk's mouth dropped open. He had just been thinking about doing that; and how did CrowWolf know that he and Moonbeam had been wanting a child? Hummingbird must have told him, he decided, as he went to find Moonbeam to share the crow feather and blessing with her.

At first Raven was upset when the guards refused to leave this new community. They had never been treated with such kindness and respect before. Raven could appreciate that. If she were honest with herself, she also liked being honored as this people's Medicine Woman. She had no Feathered Trumpet to contend with, and thus blossomed as a thoughtful and gifted healer. The People looked to her for guidance and leadership.

75

She remembered the day the elderly woman, Gentle Breeze, brought her the most beautiful grouping of feathers she had ever seen. "My grandmother was a Medicine Woman and passed these on to me, hoping that I would continue in her path. But I have not been blessed with the healing touch. So I cannot think of a better way to continue my Grandmother's energy and good work, them to pass the feathers on to you, Raven. You have helped many of us, and we do not know how to thank you. My daughter and many other women are over grieving for their dead husbands because you brought us these fine and noble men. We now have many new ones on the way, so our community will continue to grow. Thank you. May these feathers bless you."

Raven was deeply touched by the gift. The colorful feathers had a certain peace about them. However her mind was not satisfied completely, because they were not the Sacred Feathers (which had many lifetimes of prayers added to them, and a power she had never experienced before). "Was the power from the Feathers or the one using them?" she wondered again. When Feathered Trumpet had the Feathers for a brief time, she did not remember the same energy coming from them as when Sacred One held the Feathers in front of her.

She looked again at the colorful feathers Gentle Breeze had given her. The thought came to hold them up toward the sun with both arms raised. As she did this, the wind lifted her cape, spreading it wide.

"Look!" someone shouted as they saw Raven holding the feathers in the sunlight, with her wind-swept cape making her appear almost super-human. A crowd began to form and chant some sacred tones which were meaningful to these people.

Raven felt as though she had left her body. The tones of the chant lifted her spirit so she felt as though she were floating. "Stay with our people. We need you," she heard

Gentle Breeze's voice say.

Raven asked the people to get into a circle, and she blessed each of them with the colorful feathers. What a glorious day that was, she remembered. She felt so fulfilled. "Why is this not enough?" she kept asking herself. "Why do I still think I have to have those Sacred Feathers?"

Many cycles of the seasons had passed, and Raven had remained with these good people. She was grateful to be able to share her abilities in a useful way; but the Sacred Feathers were always in the back of her mind.

🪶 🪶 🪶 🪶

"Words are symbols for ideas," began Keymyu one evening after the community had its meal together. "I will attempt to use words to express ideas about how the human mind works. When I use the word EGO, it will be referring to the aspect of the human mind that is a survival mechanism for the body, but also thinks separately from the broader picture, because it is focused in MY survival and MY desires."

"Then, when I use the word SOUL, I will be referring to our true essence, which understands the broader picture and is capable of seeing the way the Creator sees. The soul is at peace doing that which the Creator intended for it to do. It sees all roles in life as equally important and is at peace with its role, no matter how simple the task."

"The ego is not satisfied with simplicity. It will continually create visions or desires of something better. The ego always wants more. Then the ego will drive one to make those visions and desires happen a certain way. Whereas, the soul understands that insights may be just thoughts passing through, or possibilities of what might happen. As each moment passes, people change their mind, things shift, and thus the possibilities one sees today, may be different from what actually happens tomorrow."

77

"When one is focused only on thoughts of what they WANT to happen, one may miss the beauty of what is actually happening in the present moment."

"Life simply is. The way we interpret how or why it is - may be an illusion. The ego creates illusions through wants and fears. A healthy soul follows its natural path through peace, and learns how to become the OBSERVER when wants or fears come forth in the mind. From the viewpoint of the observer, the soul can make wiser choices."

"Let us look within ourselves this evening, and see if we are missing the beauty of the now, by our thoughts or desires of how we WANT life to be different. This does not mean that if an aspect of life needs improvement, one does not change it. It simply means that if our thoughts are always focused in the past or future, in wants or fears, then we often miss all that is present in the now. Let us become the OBSERVER of what our mind has been thinking lately, and see if it is of the soul (peace) or of the ego (wants and fears)."

The People became quiet and contemplated Keymyu's words.

CrowWolf finished cleansing the Sacred Feathers with smoke from sweet grass, and put them away in their special container. SunWalker wanted his son to begin helping with the care of the Sacred Feathers, and CrowWolf was delighted to assist. He was feeling inspired by their energy that morning as he walked back to his dwelling.

A woman scolding a young boy caught his attention. He noticed how the boy's gentle spirit diminished with the woman's harsh words. Suddenly the boy ran into the woods and no one followed him. So CrowWolf softly walked in the boy's direction.

As CrowWolf gently sat next to the pouting boy, he took out his hawk feathers and began to examine the casing which held them. "My mother fashioned this holder for these hawk feathers," he began. "I think she did a beautiful job, don't you?" he asked the young boy, as he held the feathers in his direction.

"Yes," said the boy, surprised that someone wanted his opinion. Then he added spontaneously, "A carving of a hawk on that casing might add to the spirit of the piece."

"That is true," commented CrowWolf, treating the boy as an equal. "I wonder who could do such an intricate carving as a hawk soaring in the wind."

"I think I could," the boy said timidly, not sure it was his place to offer.

"Could you?" responded CrowWolf with great enthusiasm. "I want the original casing to remain the same, but would like a decorated sheath to place over it, when I use these feathers in ceremony," he explained.

The young boy looked down at the ground. He wanted so much to design the new sheath for CrowWolf, but had just been scolded by his mother for wasting time on drawing and carving, when he should be making useful tools, like his older brother was doing.

CrowWolf knew the young boy's thoughts and self-doubt, since he had heard his mother's harsh words. So he asked, "How would you like to learn how I fashion my hunting tools?" Everyone in the community knew that CrowWolf's tools were superior to anyone else's.

The boy's eyes widened, "Me?" he coughed out. "You would teach me your craft?"

"Yes," CrowWolf answered. "I will tell your mother that I will need to teach you from sunrise until mid-day - each day. And during that time you can give me something in return. You can fashion my new hawk sheath and show me how you do it. We will both learn from each other," he concluded.

The young boy was happy, and yet still sad. "My mother says I should be more like my older brother, doing useful things, and building up my physical strength," he confided to CrowWolf.

"Ah," replied CrowWolf, and then added. "Would your mother have an eagle fly backward and forward like a hummingbird? Would she have a palm tree give berries like a blackberry bush?" He was glad to see the young boy smile at this analogy, knowing that the boy understood its deeper meaning. CrowWolf continued, looking straight into the boy's eyes, "You are exactly as you are because that is how the Creator wants you to be; and the Creator does not make mistakes. It is our interpretation of what we think the Creator wants, that may be mistaken," he shared.

CrowWolf continued, "The Creator knows that if everyone did only hunting, then who would make the clothes or prepare the food? If everyone did only practical things, then who would inspire the people? Carving and drawing, when done from the soul's inspiration, inspire the ones who view it. You are a great inspirer, young one; and I will call you 'Spirit Song' from now on, and tell your mother of the gifts I see in you."

The boy could not stop the tears pouring out of his eyes; but they were not tears of sorrow, they were tears of appreciation.

"It is good to be sensitive enough to cry, my friend. Those who have hardened hearts usually only use their energy to destroy or tear things down. You use your energy to create and build things up, and I am proud of you." CrowWolf put his arm around this gentle boy. "I will go now and tell your mother that I have selected you as my new apprentice. And I will call you 'Spirit Song' since you will bring much inspiration to the

People through the spirit of your work. You play the flute also, don't you?" he asked, and the boy nodded yes. "Come to my dwelling tomorrow, when the sun rises, and we will begin our exchange of service. A balanced interchange is an important part in the Law of Giving and Receiving. Believe in yourself, because I believe in you," he concluded.

CrowWolf's smile and words were so warm and genuine, that the young boy could not move as he watched this honored one walk toward his mother. "Spirit Song," he said over and over in his mind; and his heart opened with a radiance he had never felt before. He could see in his mind's eye exactly how he would fashion the hawk on CrowWolf's sheath.

After CrowWolf left his mother, she came to look for her middle son, and hugged him. She did not have to say the words, for he could feel that she was sorry and also proud of him, at the same time.

Keymyu's words that night before the evening meal, echoed what CrowWolf had shared earlier in the day with the young boy.

"The Ancients created peace in their communities by honoring the gifts that each person had. They did not expect everyone to be a perfect athlete, or the most skillful hunter, or the best garment maker. They understood how the Creative Spirit of Life gifts each of us in different ways, and it all balances itself. It is up to us to listen to our heart's song and develop what brings us joy, and what is also of service to others. The person who is gifted at taking care of children is as important as the finest hunter, storyteller, or toolmaker. Inward and outward strengths need to be balanced within personal relationships as well as within community relationships."

She continued, "The Ancients warned against gossip or criticism of others. The energy we send out in our thoughts, words, and deeds will return to us - sometimes greater than how we sent it. If you want people to be kind to you, be kind to others. If you want people to appreciate you, appreciate others. If you want people to believe in you, believe in others (and also in yourself). We cannot share with another, what we have not yet learned how to share with ourself."

"When people are not appreciated as they are, the good in them is unable to grow. A wounded soul often becomes angry or uses manipulation to get what it wants. Therefore, by showing appreciation for others, we encourage their soul to become healthy and balanced."

"All these things, the Ancients lived. Let us now take a few moments to be silent, and look at how we can honor the gifts in those we know. How can we appreciate those in our family - more. How can we encourage and support all around us - more."

While the people were silent, contemplating Keymyu's words, Hummingbird, SunWalker, Keymyu and CrowWolf joined in raising the energy of the people by adding their energy to the meditation.

"We must become lighter," Hummingbird commented to Keymyu as the People prepared for the evening meal.

"I know, " Keymyu replied. "I sense the same thing. It is almost as though the molecules of our body need to become lighter; but that makes no sense to my logical mind."

"It is something we will understand and become, later," CrowWolf responded. "Often I receive information that only makes sense later on."

"How did you get so wise?" SunWalker laughed as he hugged his son with deep love.

"It is from you and everyone who has lived before us," CrowWolf replied. "When I am open, I can experience the understanding of all that has been experienced before. The Consciousness which created life, knows all that has been experienced."

The four of them nodded in agreement, and then joined the people in the evening meal. Their community was getting closer and stronger every day.

Feathered Trumpet (now Brave One) was honored at this evening's meal because he and his newly trained hunting group had killed the yellow-brown spotted beast, and brought it back to the community. The people were grateful because now they would no longer be afraid when leaving the village to gather food.

Many cycles of the seasons had passed and the elderly leader was still alive. He was training his son to take over when he passed to the Land of Living Light. "Why am I not being trained to take over as leader?" thought Brave One, as he sat down to eat. "I am the strongest, and can run faster than any man here. Why does one always have to be born in a certain lineage in order to get the opportunity to become leader? Have I not trained these boys to be men, and to kill the beast that threatened the village?"

His thoughts were interrupted by people crowding around their leader, who had slumped forward and then fell to the ground. It was the leader's son who announced that his father was gone. This particular people burned the body of one who had crossed over. The ceremony took several days. Brave One did all the appropriate things, but his thoughts were really on how he should be the leader.

On the final day of grieving, the son spoke to his people. "My father's wishes were that we remain a peaceful people. Many of our men have learned new skills of how to hunt and kill. My father's last words to me, on the morning of his passing, were: 'Let us never use these hunting and killing skills on each other, or on other humans. We were created to balance and protect Mother Earth and all She gives to us.' If he were here, he would tell you that the leader he chose, was someone who would continue to bring harmony - not only to our people, but also to the environment where we live. I will strive to continue my father's wishes, and ask you to join me in fulfilling his request." The people raised their hands in acceptance of the new leader's words.

Everyone agreed, except Brave One. "We need to conquer other people and other territory to become more powerful," he fumed in his mind. "We were created to dominate over other living creatures; and the strongest one in nature's world is always the leader. You foolish people - I am the one who should lead! I know more than anyone else here!" Brave One shouted in his thoughts.

"Then why have the people not asked you to lead them?" asked one of the young boys who first brought Brave One to this village.

Brave One jerked backward. Had this boy read his mind, he wondered. No, he must have read the anger on my face, he reasoned. But the young boy kept looking at him pensively, and then said, "Our people have always looked at a leader as one who brings harmony, because anyone who would bring dis-harmony would cause fights among the people until we destroyed each other, and then there would be no village left. You have taught us many good things about hunting and protecting ourselves, Brave One." The boy continued, "But until you have the peace and welfare of the community as your highest goal, then people will not see you as a leader." The boy's mother interrupted him by taking his hand and leading him back to their dwelling.

Brave One sat there and pondered the boy's words. "Peace and the welfare of the people have not been my goals. I suppose my motives were more for glorifying myself, and showing how powerful I was," he admitted. Then visions of the people fighting in his old village, filled his mind. He remembered their hateful words toward him and the destruction they were beginning to do to the village. "Did I cause those people to be rebellious and fight each other?" he asked himself, and then forced the answer away. "No, peace is boring," he decided. "There is no adventure in peace. I would rather have power than peace," he concluded, and began gathering his hunting things. He decided to leave this village for a while, and let the people see how well they did without him. He had heard of another village to the North. Maybe the people in that village will like adventure more than peace. When he left, he made sure that everyone saw him.

"A healthy soul allows the mind to become silent, now and then," began SunWalker one evening at the fire. "Through silence and peace, a soul can balance itself."

"When one allows certain thoughts to take over the mind and control it, then silence and peace are difficult to find. To meditate, one has to want peace above all else. The human mind and imagination can create many diversions to keep the mind from becoming still. The human ego will see peace as boring and unproductive. The ego prefers power, possessions and continual activity...anything that will puff itself up. The ego creates thoughts of ME. Inner Wisdom brings forth the understanding of WE."

"Tonight we will look within ourselves to observe any compulsive or obsessive thoughts which may be keeping us out of peace. For example, if one feels driven to have, do, or be something, one may ask if this is from the soul or the ego. The soul's path may be to explore a certain avenue in life because it brings one's heart joy, and also serves others. The ego will fester, worry, scheme, manipulate or dominate to get what it wants. There is no peace in the ego's realm. There IS peace in the soul's realm. Which will you chose: peace or war, love or fear?"

SunWalker concluded with, "Let us be quiet and go within now, to look at what has been occupying our thoughts lately, and whether the experience is from the soul or the ego." Everyone sat quietly as they looked within.

🖋 🖋 🖋 🖋

Raven did not like the feeling of anxiousness that she was feeling this morning. She tried to quiet her mind, but kept sensing that some kind of danger was approaching. She tried walking in nature to calm down. She tried bathing in the stream to calm down; but the anxiety seemed to grow and grow.

When Raven unconsciously knocked over the container with the morning meal in it, Gentle Breeze went over and softly touched her shoulder. "What is wrong, Raven? You seem agitated and worried."

Raven shook her head and sat down. "I can not figure out what is happening to me," she began. "I have not felt this way in a long time. I have been getting these strange thoughts that our community needs to move."

"But why would we do that?" asked Gentle Breeze. "We are so peaceful here."

"That's just it," Raven continued. "I feel as though something or someone is coming that will destroy the peace."

"What could that possibly be?" inquired Gentle Breeze.

"I don't know," replied Raven. "That is what bothers me. Something that I will not be able to control is coming, and

I do not know what it is, or why I am feeling this way."

"Let me talk with the counsel," Gentle Breeze suggested. "And I will see if anyone else has been feeling anything unusual."

By mid-day, Gentle Breeze had gathered six people and brought them to Raven's dwelling. "All of these people have been having similar feelings, but thought they were the only ones feeling that way," explained Gentle Breeze.

"So seven people in this village feel that we need to leave and move to another place?" Raven asked.

A soft-spoken man with long white hair responded, "Perhaps if we leave some of our supplies and dwellings here, and then travel for a bit on a sacred quest to understand these troubled feelings, then we will not have destroyed the possibility of returning home, if the cycle of unrest passes."

"A very wise proposition," Raven agreed. "Perhaps a short journey away from this place will clear our minds; and then we will not have closed the door to returning here, if it feels right."

All nodded their heads in agreement. Now who was going to tell the people? They asked Raven to prepare a ceremony where she would share how a short journey would be good for the community. "A sacred quest into the mountains to the East would help strengthen the health and prosperity of the people," Raven shared with them at the ceremonial fire that evening. Little did she know who was watching and listening in the bushes nearby.

Brave One had come upon this village, and immediately recognized his guards with their new mates and children. It was not long before he spotted Raven talking with a group of men and women. "So where are the Sacred Feathers?" he wondered. "Perhaps I'll stay hidden until I see where you keep them, Raven. And then I will reclaim what is mine, and take over these people," he sneered.

However, at the ceremonial fire that evening, he saw Raven holding a group of brightly colored feathers, and heard her convince the community that they needed to take a sacred journey up into the mountains to the East. "I can wait until you reveal the Sacred Feathers," Brave One whispered to himself. "There is no use showing myself now. My guards look like they are too satisfied, in this new way of living, to want to follow me and conquer more. Besides, what do I have to offer them in order to get them to follow me. Nothing," he frowned. "Would they follow me if I had the Sacred Feathers?" he wondered. "I would have to show that I was invincible with them first. And then I would punish anyone who did not follow my commands. Yes, that is how I will do it," he decided. "but I will have to wait and get those Sacred Feathers, first."

So Brave One went off to hunt and gather food which he would need to take on the journey, as he secretly followed these people into the mountains.

CrowWolf had been meditating in the mountains, seeking an answer to the questions his young friends were asking him. He did not feel experienced enough to answer them, and his meditation this morning only brought peace - not answers. As he put away his hawk feathers, he admired the casing Spirit Song had made for him.

Returning to the glistening valley, he searched for his father. SunWalker was digging a large hole about as deep as he was tall. "What are you doing?" inquired CrowWolf.

"Keymyu has asked me to dig an area that is as deep as a man is tall, and wide enough for a garden," SunWalker answered. "She says that she feels some strong winds are coming which will blow away our garden if it is above the ground. With the garden lower than the winds, it will be safer," he continued. "The idea seemed strange to me at first; but Keymyu is usually correct, so who am I to question," he smiled at his son.

"Father," began CrowWolf. "Would you have a few minutes to answer a question that the boys my age have been asking, but I do not know how to answer?"

"Of course," replied SunWalker as he dusted off a large rock and sat down.

"I have heard it said," began CrowWolf, "that the Sacred Ones in the past could rise above the desire for sex. Is this correct? And if they did, are we supposed to do that also? The boys have been having strong desires for mating and cannot clear their minds of it."

SunWalker laughed, "I remember those feelings well. You see, my son, humans have been designed to have natural feelings of wanting to mate when their bodies have fully matured, and a woman is able to begin a baby in her body. As people get older, and their bodies become weaker, nature begins to diminish the desire for mating."

He continued, "What the spiritual teachers of the past neglected to tell the people was that they knew how to meditate; and the more one meditates, the more one releases the attachment to physical senses. The less attachment one has to the senses, the less they desire sex. Are you following?" CrowWolf nodded.

"However, since the average person did not know how to meditate, then of course it was difficult for them to silence nature's natural desires. Selfish people often took sex whenever they wanted, no matter who it hurt." He paused to think how to phrase what he wanted to say next. "A wise community teaches their young the awesome responsibility that comes with mating, because a seed of a new being may be planted within a woman during mating. Who will take care of the newborn if the parents are too young? Therefore, with each mating, it is wise to have decided that if a new child is the result, then the ones who mated will take responsibility for the care of that child. And the care of a child is a lifetime commitment!"

"So mating may mean that one will have a lifetime commitment as a result of their action," surmised CrowWolf. "That would certainly make me think carefully before following a physical urge," he decided.

SunWalker smiled. "Meditating lessens all sorts of addictions to the senses: addictions to food, sleep, the desire for power, fear...and so forth." He could see that his son had enough to think about, so added, "How would you like to help me dig this hole?"

"Of course, Father," CrowWolf responded and began helping SunWalker.

Raven's community enjoyed the brisk air and higher vibration of the mountains. They had spent a full moon cycle there when one of the boys brought Raven a clear, sharp, long stone, that glistened in the sunlight. She immediately noticed an energy from the stone as she held it. "Where did you find this?" Raven asked.

"It was down in a valley about half a day's journey away. I was exploring some caves with my friends, and the sunlight through a crack hit this and created colors. Let me show you," said the boy as he held the crystal in such a way that the reflected light created a rainbow of color.

"Ohhh," sighed Raven, and took the stone back from the boy. "Show me the caves where you found this."

90

A small group of people followed Raven and the boy to the cave; and Brave One carefully stalked them from behind. "Look over here," called one of the children. "There must have been other people here because there is a woven mat on the ground." Everyone went over to the place where the mat was. Raven then found a woven bracelet next to it. Her mind remembered the woven bracelet on the young girl that was going to be sacrificed long ago on the Great Mound. "Could it be? Have I found the people with the Sacred Feathers?" she wondered. She asked a few trusted friends to search the area without involving the rest of the village.

Hummingbird saw shadows of figures coming closer and closer to her village, in her meditation that morning. A hawk swooped down and shrieked its call very near to where she was sitting. "It is time," she heard within. "You know what you have to do."

Hummingbird had been having that old dream almost every night lately. The details of what she would do were very clear in it. When she awoke, she quickly went off to meditate and calm her mind. However, when her meditation gave her the same message as the dream, she knew that today was the day. Quickly, she returned to the village and gathered what was needed.

Keymyu found one of Hummingbird's crow feathers with a shell on it, at her sleeping mat, as she returned from her morning walk. She noticed a crow feather on SunWalker's sleeping mat also. Moonbeam, Hawk and several other people were also carrying Hummingbird's crow feathers. "What is going on?" she wondered.

"Hummingbird left a while ago, after telling me where to place all her crow feathers," explained Moonbeam as she approached Keymyu.

"What do you mean left? Where is she going?" asked Keymyu.

"I don't know," sighed Moonbeam, "All she would say was: sometimes the actions of one will save the many. What does that mean? I'm so worried."

"So am I," said Keymyu. She wondered if the crow feathers were a final goodbye from Hummingbird, but did not want to alarm Moonbeam with that possibility. "Something strange is in the air. It reminds me of the time when I was almost sacrificed on that Great Mound." Keymyu stopped suddenly, and questioned within: Am I feeling the energy of the people who were on the Great Mound that day? "Where is SunWalker!" she barked at Moonbeam.

"Somewhere with CrowWolf, I think," replied Moonbeam, startled by Keymyu's abruptness.

"Gather the people quickly, we need to have a counsel meeting," Keymyu ordered with an urgency which was unlike her usual manner.

Moonbeam got Hawk to help her find the people of the counsel. They found everyone but Laughing Wolf and Hummingbird. Keymyu attempted to explain, as calmly as she could, what she sensed might be coming.

🪶 🪶 🪶 🪶

Laughing Wolf felt something strange in the way Hummingbird was almost sneaking around the village that morning. He watched her go in and out of dwellings, looking around to see if anyone saw her. His keen sense of knowing that something was needed before it happened, caused him to follow her, from a distance.

She came to a ridge that had a steep drop, and then disappeared over the edge. "What is she doing?" he wondered and went to the edge of the ridge to find her. However, Hummingbird was no were in sight, and the cliff was too steep to climb down. Suddenly, he noticed a small swatch of Hummingbird's cape caught on a bush over the edge of the cliff. "Oh no, Hummingbird," Wolf cried, and fell to his knees.

When Raven saw how large the community was in this glimmering valley, she decided that a small group of men would not be strong enough to retrieve the Feathers. She would have to take all the guards, and then capture someone valuable in exchange for the Sacred Feathers. How would she surprise them? That was the question.

However, when Raven returned to that village with all her guards, there were only a few people wandering in the center area. "Where did all the people go?" she wondered. Her old ruthlessness about getting the Feathers had returned.

Keymyu had emptied the village, leaving only her, Moonbeam, Hawk, SunWalker and CrowWolf behind. She told the people where they needed to go for safety. She, and these four people were gathering all the sacred items they used for ceremony. They were completely surprised when Raven and her guards surrounded them, and they were out-numbered ten to one.

Why did she not keep the men with them while gathering the sacred items, Keymyu scolded herself, but remembered how SunWalker thought that the men should stay with the rest of the community to protect them. He probably thought her concerns were a false alarm.

Raven grabbed Moonbeam and pointed a sharp knife at her large belly, which held her soon-to-arrive baby. Hawk instinctively lunged for Raven, but was beaten down by three men. SunWalker tried to assist with his kicks, but was also stopped by more men than he could handle.

Keymyu spoke up to stop the bloodshed. "What do you want?" she asked, already knowing the answer, and wishing it were not right here with them.

"The Sacred Feathers," sneered Raven, as she handed her knife and Moonbeam over to one of her men. Then she suddenly began rummaging through the containers the group had been carrying, and came upon the special container that she recognized as the holder of the Sacred Feathers. "Ahhh," Raven sighed. "It looks as though I have arrived just in time." But when she opened the holder, it was empty, so she threw it on the ground.

Keymyu instantly bent down and picked it up, but was shocked to find it empty. "The Feathers!" she exclaimed. "Where are they?" SunWalker and CrowWolf quickly looked inside the holder. They looked at each other, and then at Keymyu. All three suddenly understood Hummingbird's disappearance.

Raven discerned that they knew something, but were not telling her. She grabbed a guard's knife, and held it against Keymyu's throat. Then she sliced her skin so blood trickled down, to show she meant business.

"Hummingbird," CrowWolf spoke up.

"No!" shouted SunWalker.

"Yes," answered CrowWolf. "We can tell you who took the Feathers, but not where she is. She left the village early this morning."

"Is that all you can tell me," Raven demanded, drawing blood again from Keymyu's throat.

"Yes!" CrowWolf said emphatically; and Raven could tell that this young boy was too frightened to lie.

"Guards!" Raven commanded. "Search the area. Not for a whole group of foot prints, but for a single pair of foot-prints

...small...a woman's size. Tie these five up first." The guards tied the captives and sat them down. It was not long before someone yelled from a distance, "A woman...going this way. Come quickly."

Raven had her men force the captives to come also. They made their way to a clearing where the earth sloped down and ended in a steep cliff. There at the edge of the cliff stood a woman with reddish hair. Her cape blew in the wind, and she held a torch with fire in her hand.

"Mother!" CrowWolf shouted, as he watched Hummingbird struggle to keep her balance at the edge of the cliff.

Just then Hummingbird called out, "If my People cannot keep the Feathers, then no one can have them. I will not allow the Sacred Feathers to be misused by anyone with selfish motives." With those last words, Hummingbird quickly pulled out the Sacred Feathers and lit them with the torch. The fire also caught her cape, blowing in the wind, and she screamed as she disappeared over the edge of the cliff.

"Hummingbird!" screamed Moonbeam as she kicked the guard in his groin and raced to the edge of the cliff. By the time everyone arrived at the edge, only the burning cape could be seen at the bottom. Moonbeam fell on the ground sobbing hysterically, and Hawk tried to comfort her the best he could with his hands tied. SunWalker used a sharp rock to free himself, and then freed CrowWolf and Keymyu. CrowWolf then freed Hawk and Moonbeam, while SunWalker comforted Keymyu. He wanted to make sure the cuts on her throat were not serious.

Raven stood looking over the cliff, numb and in a daze. All her dreams and hopes had just gone over that ledge in a blaze of fire. Her guards followed her as she returned back to her people in the mountains, with an empty heart. The people who had the Feathers were of no interest to her now that they no longer had the Feathers.

Brave One watched all this with shock and dismay. How was he going to take over without the Sacred Feathers for his power and authority. His only hope was to persuade the former guards that he could give them more than Raven could give them. So he followed Raven and her men back to their community in the mountains. "I will watch and wait for just the right opportunity," he decided.

"You were very convincing," smiled Laughing Wolf.

"And it was a good thing you were here to make sure I landed on this ledge. You pulled me in quickly," sighed Hummingbird in relief.

"The burning cape singed your hair," commented Laughing Wolf. "I did not like that part of the plan. It was very risky."

"But I had to make them believe that the Sacred Feathers were gone," emphasized Hummingbird. "Otherwise those people would continue to hunt us down, trying to capture the Feathers."

"I do not think you would have landed on this ledge without me grabbing you," Wolf kept shaking his head, glad the drama was over.

"You always have a knack of being there when people need you," said Hummingbird. "I am glad you followed me, and offered to help...once I showed you that I had not fallen over the cliff." She smiled, then added. "How long do you think we need to stay here before it will be safe to let our People know what I really did."

"We better wait a few days," said Wolf. "And then I will sneak out and make sure all of the enemy has gone."

Hummingbird agreed, and sat down next to the food supplies she had stored in this alcove. "I hope Moonbeam will forgive me for not telling her what I was going to do."

"And what about CrowWolf?" Wolf asked. "How will he take your death?"

"I don't know," Hummingbird replied. "I'll send him some thoughts that I am still alive." So she centered her mind and went into the realm where all souls meet.

CrowWolf was in a fog after he freed Hawk and Moonbeam. His mother had often said to him that giving one's life for one's People was one of the greatest gifts to share, but he did not realize she would sacrifice herself like she did.

He told SunWalker that he wanted to go off and be by himself for a short while. SunWalker did not know if that was such a good idea, after what had just happened; but his son had turned and left before he could respond. Keymyu grabbed SunWalker's arm and asked him to help her and Hawk lift Moonbeam. The pains in Moonbeam's belly were getting stronger. Perhaps giving birth will take Moonbeam's mind off her sister's death, Keymyu hoped. SunWalker was torn between following his son, or helping take care of this screaming woman. He knew that Moonbeam needed him more right now, so he helped carry her back to the village. Then he went to bring the rest of the community back, so the women could help Moonbeam with her birthing.

CrowWolf was far away by the time Moonbeam gave birth. He had started traveling North, and kept walking and walking. The sun was setting before he had to sit down because his legs ached so much.

CrowWolf picked some nuts and berries nearby and then sat back, placing the hawk feather case on his chest for comfort. He had no more tears to cry; they nearly blinded him as he tried to walk that day.

The Feathers on his chest gave off a surge of energy. CrowWolf decided to open his satchel and take them out. "The Sacred Feathers!" he screamed. "So you didn't burn them after all, Mother. You must have used my hawk feathers, which look like these from a distance. Then maybe you didn't really fall over the cliff!" He remembered that all he saw was his mother's cape burning at the bottom of the cliff. "Mother!" He found himself laughing and crying at the same time. Then he remembered to thank the hawk for offering its feathers. "I am sorry that we burned your fine feathers, hawk spirit. Thank you for your sacrifice for Our People."

A gray wolf caught his attention as it appeared from behind some trees. When CrowWolf followed its gaze, he saw a crow sitting in a tree. "My two companions," sighed Crow-Wolf. "You are always there when I need you." The crow flew North, and the wolf followed. CrowWolf hobbled around a corner after them. There he saw the wolf standing by a dead deer. The wolf then disappeared into the woods, and Crow-Wolf thanked the deer for the nourishment it provided.

"I will make sure to leave some food for you, Wolf and Crow," CrowWolf said in his thoughts. An alcove in the rocks provided a good place for CrowWolf to sleep. He knew that the wolf would stand guard while he rested. "Mother," he sighed as he fell off to sleep.

Raven could not eat or sleep. "You must eat," pleaded Gentle Breeze, concerned with how gray Raven's skin looked.

"There is no reason to live," sighed Raven.

"What do you mean? We need you. You are our Medicine Woman and leader." Gentle Breeze put the crystal on Raven's forehead and then on her heart. "May the pulse you

98

felt from this open your desire to live," prayed Gentle Breeze.

Raven's eyes widened. She took the crystal from Gentle Breeze's hand and placed it on her forehead again. "I can see that cave where the crystals are," she explained. "I need to go there for some reason." Raven sat up. "Would you bring me some broth. I need some nourishment before I go."

"Gladly!" smiled Gentle Breeze. She was happy to see some life come back into Raven's eyes.

After eating and packing some things for the journey, Raven headed off for the cave where the young boy had found the crystals. She did not realize that someone was following her. The opening of the cave was not very big, but after a short tunnel, it expanded into a larger area. Raven held her torch high and looked for a place to sit. A crack between two rocks supported her torch. She closed her eyes and began focusing on her breath. Her mind seemed to clear easily here. She felt peace for the first time in a long time.

There was a rumbling noise in the distance. Could that be thunder? She did not remember any storm clouds in the sky on her way there. Suddenly a large crash jolted her eyes open, and stones began to cascade down from the direction of the cave entrance.

Raven grabbed her torch and raced to the entrance to see what was happening. It was completely closed. No sunlight could be seen. Panic filled her mind. "What happened? Am I trapped in here? How will I get out of here? How could the opening to the cave have closed?"

She tried to take deep breaths to calm herself. "There must be another way out of here. Stay calm," she tried to reassure herself. Slowly she worked her way back to the larger area and then began to explore every passageway she could find. "Please do not let my torch go out," she prayed.

After what seemed like a long time, she explored the last passageway, but there was no exit to be found. "Great

Spirit," Raven pleaded, "Do not let me die this way. Show me a way out of here." She sat down in an area where the crystals were the most prevalent and closed her eyes to try to calm her mind.

Memories of standing in the wind came to her. She was holding the colorful Medicine Feathers high, and the people in her village were singing tones which made her feel like she was floating. Then she remembered the vision she had as a young girl, in which she was leading people with Feathers in her hand. Could the feathers from Gentle Breeze be the Feathers in my vision?" she wondered. "Was that my destiny... to be with the people I am with now, instead of having the Sacred Feathers?"

She then remembered how good it felt to be appreciated and honored in her new village. Gentle Breeze had become the nurturing mother she had never had, because her mother died when she was a baby. Even the guards appreciated her more in that village. They had learned to respect her advice because she did not have to scheme and manipulate the way she did when Feathered Trumpet was around.

The energy of the crystals were allowing her to look at her life as an observer and see the motives behind all her decisions and actions. She did not like observing the ruthless part of herself, such as when she drew blood from Keymyu's throat to get information about the Sacred Feathers. She could feel Keymyu's pain as though it were her own pain. Then she remembered the pain of despair she felt when the Sacred Feathers went up in flames. She suddenly realized that she had focused so hard on getting the Sacred Feathers, that when they were gone, she had no reason left to live...or so she thought. "I missed a more important reason to live," she exclaimed. "The love from people who feel like family is far more fulfilling than obtaining any object!"

"What you gave...was what you received," she heard in her mind. She saw that whenever she gave anger, she experienced the results of that anger within herself. Whenever

100

she gave healing, she experienced the positive energy of healing within herself. "What I gave IS what I received," she realized.

The air was getting thinner in the cave and Raven was feeling drowsy. She wrapped herself in her blanket and curled up to get warm. Soon she fell asleep. "What you give...is what you receive," echoed in her mind.

Brave One used a large tree branch to wedge the rock until it fell on to the opening of the cave. "There!" he said triumphantly. "Now you will know what it feels like being left behind while someone steals away your guards and becomes leader of a village. I am the one who should be their leader!" he proclaimed.

As he walked back to the campsite in the mountains where Raven's people were, he wondered how he was going to get the guards to follow him. Should he tell them a story of how Raven fell off a cliff and died? Maybe she jumped off the cliff after the Sacred Feathers? No, none of that was believable. He would have to think of something.

Laughing Wolf helped Hummingbird up the cliff after he made sure the enemy had left, and the People were safe in their village.

"How are we going to do this?" asked Wolf. "The fact that you are still alive will shock many, and I heard the cries of a new baby. I think Moonbeam had her baby."

"What if you go, Wolf, and tell them. They do not think that you are dead...just missing. Then come and get me when the time is right," suggested Hummingbird.

Wolf agreed and returned to the village, telling Sun-Walker first, who jumped up and down like a child who had just won a prize. SunWalker then told Moonbeam, Hawk and

Keymyu. Soon the rest of the village learned that Hummingbird was alive. They could not wait to hear her story.

"What about CrowWolf?" SunWalker asked. "He has been gone a long time. Has anyone seen him?" No one knew where he was.

Laughing Wolf carefully escorted Hummingbird back to the village, as the community cheered and smiled with delight. SunWalker hugged her long and hard; and Keymyu's heart skipped a beat when she learned that Hummingbird had exchanged the Sacred Feathers with CrowWolf's hawk feathers.

"Then CrowWolf has the Sacred Feathers?" Keymyu asked.

"Yes," responded Hummingbird. "but I keep sensing that he is not coming back here. It feels as though the Feathers are leading him North."

"Then I must follow him," said SunWalker.

"Me too," said Hummingbird and Keymyu at the same time.

"And I will go, also," said Hawk, but Moonbeam pulled his arm, and he looked down at her, holding their baby in her arms.

"Wait a minute," protested SunWalker. "Who is going to care for the community? We cannot leave them here without leadership."

"I will stay," volunteered Hawk. "It would be difficult for Moonbeam to travel right now, and you have carefully taught me all your skills, SunWalker."

"You will be a good leader, Hawk. And Moonbeam is a wise counselor for the women. But I would suggest that you move the community into the deepest part of the jungle in case Raven or Feathered Trumpet ever try to find us again. Their craving for power and control would hurt all the good we have developed in Our People."

"I agree," said Hawk, and Moonbeam smiled up at him.

"Will we ever see you again?" Moonbeam asked Hummingbird.

"I do not know, my good and loyal sister," Hummingbird responded. "I felt so terrible when I heard you sobbing at the edge of the cliff. But your genuine sorrow was needed to convince Raven that the Feathers and I were gone."

"You always were good at keeping secrets," her sister smirked. "We should give you an award for your performance." Everyone laughed.

"Why did you have Moonbeam give us the crow feathers?" asked Keymyu.

"There were several reasons," Hummingbird began. "I hoped you would remember how I told you that Sacred One told me to use the shells whenever I needed help. Secondly, (and forgive me for this), I was hoping you would see the crow feathers as my saying goodbye before I died."

"Well it worked," frowned Moonbeam. "I was hoping that was <u>not</u> the message."

"I thought that too," admitted Keymyu. "You sure had us convinced that you went over the cliff in a blaze of fire!" Everyone agreed, and was glad it was not so.

Gentle Breeze noticed that Raven had dropped her colorful Medicine Feathers slightly outside their campsite on the path toward the cave. "Oh no," she thought. "Raven will need these." She asked one of the guards, who had traveled with them to the cave, to bring Raven the Feathers.

He agreed, and soon was on his way. When he found the cave sealed with a large boulder, he immediately knew something was wrong. It took many attempts before he was able to move the boulder far enough where he could wedge his way inside. A light was barely flickering down one of the

103

passage ways. He followed it until he saw Raven slumped over, with her torch nearby.

Immediately he carried her to the fresh air outside the cave. "Raven, Raven," he called as he shook her and then made her walk with him, with her arm swung over his shoulder.

She opened her eyes, and the grogginess soon wore off. "How did you find me?" she asked. The guard told her about Gentle Breeze noticing that she had dropped the colorful Medicine Feathers.

"The Feathers!" Raven grabbed them, and held them to her heart. "You must be the Feathers in my vision because you saved my life!" Tears clouded her eyes, and the guard looked away to allow her to collect herself.

"Who could have done this?" he asked. "It must have been someone who is awfully strong."

"Someone who would want me dead," Raven reasoned, and remembered the anxious feelings of danger she was having right before she asked the community to go to the mountains.

"No one in our village would do this, Raven," the guard assured her. "We all respect you, and prefer your considerate way of leading over Feathered.... Do you think that Feathered Trumpet is alive, and somehow found us?"

Raven had been wondering the same thing. "If so, our village is in danger. You know his ruthless way of punishing people and taking power. We need to get back there as fast as we can." With that, they both ran back to the campsite.

Feathered Trumpet had kidnapped three women. He took one at a time, when no one was around to see him. He captured Gentle Breeze first because he had seen her with Raven and did not want the old woman to challenge his leadership. Then he took a wife of one of the guards, and a daughter of another guard. "Three people to trade for power," he said to himself. "Maybe I will keep the young girl, and trade the other two back. The girl would make a fine mate for me. These people are weak. They would do anything to save someone's life, especially after I tell them that Raven is never coming back. That will weaken their spirit," he decided.

Trumpet had tied the three women to a tree and placed dry grass and branches around the base so that he could light a fire quickly if he did not get what he wanted. "Now I will sit and wait with my torch until people come looking for their missing women."

Raven and the guard caught sight of Feathered Trumpet as he was lighting his torch. They knew that he was ruthless enough to burn the women if the two of them attempted to free the captives. "I need time to think how we can free them," Raven said, and motioned for the guard to follow her.

Suddenly she realized that feeding Trumpet's ego would create him seeing only what he wanted to see. She found one of Gentle Breeze's friends, and asked her to make a grouping of feathers that looked like her colorful Medicine Feathers. She then had the guard dig a circular pit, deep enough for him to sit in. Next she laced some branches over the top of the pit and covered the opening with a blanket. Three women sat on the corners of the blanket with items to sew or work on. This would make the blanket appear as though it were on solid ground. At the fourth corner of the blanket, Raven piled a stack of twigs. The guard in the pit would be able to stick his hand up and start a fire in those twigs at just the right moment. Raven gathered the people and told them what was going to happen and how they needed to participate to make it believable.

Finally, she was ready, and sent one of the guards to give Feathered Trumpet a message. She instructed the guard to make sure Feathered Trumpet approached her area in a specific direction so that the pit where the guard was hiding would be hidden behind the tall pile of twigs. The message to Trumpet was: "We are ready to exchange something more powerful than the Sacred Feathers for the three women. You will have to bring the women to Raven's campsite in order to see a demonstration of the power. Having these two objects will make you the most powerful person in this new land." Raven added, "If he hesitates or says NO, then tell him that these two objects were powerful enough to help me escape from the cave. Then tell him that I am willing to leave the village, and let him be the leader; but I must see the three women back with their families before I leave."

Feathered Trumpet did not like the idea of taking the three women away from the fire area he had prepared. However, when the messenger added that the objects helped Raven escape from the cave, he was intrigued. Finally, when he heard that Raven would leave the village once she knew the three women were back with their families, he decided to take a chance and listen to her proposal. "After she leaves," he thought, "I can take any woman I want; so I win no matter what." Trumpet carefully untied the women from the tree, but tied them to each other so they could barely walk. Then Raven's guard showed Trumpet the path he and the women needed to take.

Trumpet had been watching the village for a long time and had counted the men and women in it. So when he made sure all the village was in front of him and no one could ambush him from the rear, he moved the women close enough to listen to Raven's proposal. With a burning torch in one hand and his large knife in the other hand, Trumpet was ready to create as much destruction as necessary to get what he wanted.

Raven held up the imitation colored Medicine Feathers with great reverence. "These Feathers are more powerful than the Sacred Feathers, and I will give you a demonstration," she began. She held up the long clear crystal stone in her other hand and waved the Feathers over the stone, mouthing some words very softly. "Now," she said, "Look at how the energy of the Feathers creates colors through the sacred stone." She held the crystal in such a way that the reflected light created a rainbow of colors on the white sand ground.

"Ohhhhh," said the village people, well rehearsed in what to do.

Trumpet thought for a moment and then said, "So how will colors on the ground make me the most powerful leader in this new land?"

Raven was waiting for this moment, "Because the stone now has the power to create fire!" she shouted with great majesty and pointed the crystal toward the pile of twigs next to the pit where the guard ignited them on fire.

"Ahhhhh!" cried the people of the village, and the women on the blanket bowed up and down toward the fire as though the Creator had started it. Then all the people bowed at Raven chanting, "Raven, Raven, Raven."

Chills went up Feathered Trumpet's arms at all the excitement and reverence he saw in the crowds. "Would people bow to me like that if I showed such power with those sacred objects?" he wondered.

"So you will give me the Medicine Feathers and stone if I give you these three women? And you will leave the village, Raven, and let me be the leader?" Trumpet asked, still wondering why she would surrender her village.

"When I see the three women back with their families, and you promise that you will be a kind leader; then I will give them to you. But I must also have one last evening with my people to say goodbye. And tomorrow morning I will share the secret words that need to be said with the Feathers to make the stone powerful enough to create fire."

"Tell me the words now!" demanded Feathered Trumpet.

107

"No," said Raven defiantly. "Then we will have nothing to bargain. I need to see that you treat my people with respect tonight, before I share the final part of the exchange in the morning. Release the three women now, and I will hand over the Feathers and stone, at the same time."

Trumpet eyed her suspiciously. "We will do the exchange at the same time," he agreed. As he freed the women, and they ran to their loved ones, Raven handed him the Feathers and stone. They seemed like just an ordinary stone and feathers to him. He tried waving the Feathers over the stone, and then pointing the stone at something to see if it burned.

"The secret words make them come alive," repeated Raven, as she watched his actions. Before Trumpet could protest any further, the people began bowing at Trumpet and chanting, "Great One, Great One, Great One..." Trumpet liked the sound of that. This would be his new name, he decided.

"These people already see you as their leader, since you now possess the Feathers and stone," commented Raven to boost his ego further.

Feathered Trumpet never had this much attention in his old village. "No wonder Raven has these people in the palm of her hand," he decided. "She has these powerful Feathers and stone to keep the people in line. I wonder if I pointed the stone at a person, if they would catch on fire," he mused.

The women led him to an area where all sorts of food and drink were laid out. The guards saluted him with their drinks and hugged their women. "Which one of these women will I choose?" thought Feathered Trumpet as he eyed each one of them.

Some boys were playing behind Trumpet, so he could hear their words while he ate. "I think I know where Raven got that sacred stone," said one of them, and Trumpet strained his ears to hear. "There is a cave not far from here. I saw Raven go into it, and when she came out, she had that stone," the boy continued. "I bet there are other stones just like it in that cave. I will take you there in the morning," the boy concluded. "A cave? Could it be that the cave where I trapped Raven was the secret place where she found the sacred stone? Could there be more there? Of course, there are," he finally realized. "That is why it has been so easy to take over this village. Raven knows that she can go to the cave and get more stones. I am going to have to find a way to seal that cave up again, or take all the stones out of it for myself. Imagine how powerful I would be if I were the only one who had access to the stones. I could trade them for whatever I wanted."

Trumpet did not realize that he was laughing out loud, and everyone was looking at him. "This drink is good!' he explained. "I will be right back." Casually, he got up from the feast, carrying his sword and torch, and walked off to the woods as though he were going to relieve himself. Then Trumpet crossed over to the path which led to the cave. "Perhaps the real reason why Raven wanted this extra night was so that she could just disappear with all the stones, and I would never have the words needed to bring power to my stone. I need to see what is in that cave," he decided and was glad he had brought his torch.

Raven and three of her guards watched him leave. They were hoping that the boy's words would peak Trumpet's curiosity. As they began to follow Trumpet, the wind suddenly picked up. With each step, the wind got stronger and stronger. Black clouds began to swirl in the distance. "I think we need to go back and have our people bring their things to the cave on the other side of the mountain," Raven yelled to her guards through the roaring wind. "Forget about Trumpet. If he keeps heading in that direction, he will head right into those dark swirling clouds. Helping the people is more important right now." The guards agreed, and they turned back toward the campsite. The people were already packing their things and heading to the cave for cover.

Trumpet pushed his way against the wind. Nothing was going to keep him from becoming the most powerful person in this new land. "A sacred rock that creates fire and can even move large boulders!" he gloated. "What else can it do?" he wondered.

It seemed like forever before Trumpet got to the cave. He waited until he was inside before he lit his torch. The winds roared and swirled outside the cave as Trumpet moved through the main passage into an area that was filled with glimmering rocks. He did not care what the wind was doing. The sight of all these crystals was more than he expected. He imagined all the possessions he could trade for these valuable stones. As he chipped away to collect them, he did not notice the tumbling, whirling and crashing that was going on outside.

As the great wind ripped away trees by their roots, the ground gave way above the entrance of the cave. Dirt, rocks and branches began to pile up in front of the cave. Soon there was a mound of rubble so high that the entrance of the cave was totally sealed.

Trumpet became weary after a while from all his work, loosening the stones. He yawned and rubbed his eyes. "Perhaps I need to rest for awhile, and then continue," he decided and fell asleep. As the air thinned in the cave, the torch went out.

Feathered Trumpet's dreams took him through his whole life. He felt all the pain that he caused others. He saw how his selfishness turned people away from him. His final thought was: "What I gave...caused what I received."

Keymyu and Moonbeam ran to the garden after the storm with high winds ended. "The garden is safe!" laughed

Keymyu as she looked down into the large pit which Sun-Walker had dug.

"So it is!" agreed Moonbeam. "I will pick some things for your journey North with SunWalker and Hummingbird. We will miss you greatly, but know that you will share the Sacred Ways wherever you go."

Keymyu hugged her dear friend. She did not want to tell her how she had been having feelings that the storms would become worse. She sensed floods and fire ravaging the land. Then suddenly she remembered something that would be helpful. "Moonbeam, I tell you this in case you need to use it. If the People need to find a place of refuge, listen for a whistling sound in the wind; and then follow that sound to a place where there is a hole in a rock, through which the wind is whistling. Look below that rock with a hole in it, and there will be a cave where you will be safe."

Moonbeam understood that Keymyu was telling her something very important because she felt chills on her arms. She had also sensed that the recent storms were just the beginning of some major changes. She knew that living the Sacred Way with a peaceful mind and kindness in one's heart, helped one remain centered so that they knew what to do as needed.

"Pass on the Sacred Ways to as many people as you meet." Keymyu added, "And I will do the same. A blessing from the Sacred Feathers will go to everyone who passes on information about the Sacred Ways to others. People of the Earth must return to living in harmony with the Earth, if they are to survive. Self-centered thoughts keep one in the self-destructive realm of ME. Seeing how our every thought, word and action affects the balance of everything around us - is a sign that one understands the wisdom of WE. All is interconnected. We need each other; we balance each other; we are all apart of the Creator's creation. As CrowWolf said: 'The

Creator does not make mistakes. It is our interpretation of what is happening which may be mistaken.' All extremes will eventually balance themselves, and Mother Earth may bring about a balance which will bring humans back into harmony with the Earth."

Moonbeam smiled and nodded. "As we listen within, we will know what to do."

🪶 🪶 🪶 🪶

CrowWolf awoke with thoughts of his Mother clearly in his mind. "It feels like you are well, Mother. I want to return to our village, but the crow, wolf and Feathers are urging me to go North. Feel my love for you and Father. I need to follow my destiny." Thus CrowWolf continued heading North, following the crow and wolf.

He sensed that his family might be following after him. His dream last night showed him a new group of people that he would meet, and join, and share the Sacred Feathers with. He sensed that he would be eating less meat to keep his energy and consciousness lighter, and thus more open for receiving information as needed. The new land where he was going needed the energy of the Feathers for all that was going to happen there. The Feathers would draw those who would work together to help humanity grow in light and return to the Sacred Ways of honoring Mother Earth and each other as a sacred part of the Creator's creation.

"What you give...is what you receive," he heard in his mind, and it felt as though the words were coming from the Feathers. CrowWolf realized that whoever had come in contact with the Sacred Feathers, experienced that lesson. If they gave out disharmony, they received disharmony. If they gave out peace, they experienced peace. If they helped others grow in light, they also grew in light...and became lighter in their heart and soul.

NAMASTÉ

AUTHOR'S NOTE:

This story was inspired by Golden Eagle Medicine Feathers that came into my life. All I knew was that they were very old and from the Crow Nation. My heart began to tell me that they needed to return to their original People, but I did not know how to find them. The words: "Take me home," kept coming into my mind.

Then, out of nowhere, a member of the Crow Nation showed up in my life. His name is Yellow Eagle, and he comes from a long line of Chiefs and Medicine Men. The synchronicity of a Crow native with the name of Yellow Eagle (Golden Eagle) appearing in my life, caught my attention.

I decided to talk with him and sense the sincerity of his heart, before I told him anything about the Feathers. After a couple of hours of conversation, I felt an honor and compassion in his heart, so I casually asked if he ever had the feeling of any special Feathers coming into his life. He responded that I was the second person who had said something about special Feathers coming into his life. He did not think anything about it because eagle feathers continually came into his life. But a person, whom he greatly respected, said that there was a glowing light around the special Feathers soon to arrive.

My mouth dropped open, and he asked me why. So I told him about the Feathers I had. I had sensed something very sacred and powerful about them. They were in a very old casing with knots tied in the fringe.

It became very clear to me that this was the person who was supposed to receive the Feathers for the Crow People. We had a short ceremony together, and when Yellow Eagle spoke the Crow language and gave thanks, an air of electricity filled the room. The hair on my arms stood out, and I felt tingles all over my body. A sacredness filled my heart, and I felt blessed to be there.

When Yellow Eagle finished what he was saying in the Crow language, he translated for me. He had spontaneously adopted me as "daughter" and gave me the name "Known By Her Papers," which his aunt Winona (Dress That Became Old) later changed to "Known By Her Powerful Papers."

At first, we thought it referred to my art; but soon after this ceremony, a story began in my mind. I remember commenting to him that I wished I knew how to write a movie script because I was seeing and feeling a story which felt like it was about these very Feathers.

One morning words began to come, so I stopped what I was doing, and began to write them down. I had never woven characters and plot together before, so I just trusted the words and feelings which came through me as the story unfolded.

As each character was described, I felt as though I was living inside them and could feel how they were feeling. As I moved from character to character, a little bit more of the story was revealed. It reminded me that we each have only a piece of the whole picture; and when we take time to listen to another person's perspective, our view of the whole broadens. What divides us is when we think that our way is the best way or the only way. Humility often reminds us that we only know our point of view - and all points of view make up the Whole.

The Feathers seem to be gathering people of like-mind, who feel that honoring all races and treating each other with reverence will help bring healing to the world. I hope this story inspires you to "grow in light" and listen to your Inner Wisdom.

Remember that the story is a PARABLE, or a fictitious narrative which may bring spiritual truths. Some people have commented that it feels as though the story is about the future, rather than the past.

The People with the Sacred Feathers are mystical people who feel compelled to follow Inner Wisdom rather than man-made rules which create separation, superiority, and thus conflict. The reason they hold together as loving friends is because they choose to honor men and women with equal reverence, and they also choose to honor people of different races and beliefs. Those who see themselves as superior or want control, create their own self-destruction. Those who glimpse the peace that comes from healing the feelings of separation with others, eventually grow and change and live in peace.

The time is NOW! Spend more time in meditation or prayer, and remember a reverence for Mother Earth and every aspect of Creation. May kindness and harmlessness be your motto. May you choose to bless others rather than criticize them. May you replace any negative thoughts with the experience of God's Love.

A second book suddenly began to come forth after another prayer circle with the Feathers. I hope it will shed light on how we can heal the sense of separation between us.

Thank you for passing the message of this book on to people around the world. A blessing is being sent forth every day to everyone involved with sharing the message of these "Papers." ALL IS WELL. Return to peace.

Blessings,

TORI

THANK YOU TO:

The Creator of All That Is;
Don, my husband and best friend;
Gilbert and Ann, for encouraging equality among all people;
Maddie Kay, for your Inner Guidance;
Joyce, Joe, Bonnie, Luckie, Marita, and Ruth, for your loving
 support;
Cheryl, for your patience with the typesetting;
The Ancient Ones who shared this story with me;
and all Beings of Light who are encouraging us to heal the
 separation between us and return to the Sacred Ways which
 honor the Creator, Mother Earth, and every aspect of
 Creation.

Recommended Viewing:
AWAKENING TO ZERO POINT
(1-800-243-1438 OR 206-455-1053)

Recommended Listening:
to your Inner Wisdom which leads to peace,
harmony, health, wholeness and kindness

Recommended moving meditation: T'ai Chi Chih
Certified Instructor: Don Fiore 1-888-443-4677
http:\\www.taichichih.org

For more copies of this book:
Fiore, P.O. Box 50663, Phoenix, AZ 85076
(Shipping and Handling: $3.00 per book.
Discounts for volume orders)